CU00921890

# SHOTGUNS
## THEIR HISTORY AND DEVELOPMENT

by
Major Hugh B. C. Pollard

**Read Country Books**
Home Farm
44 Evesham Road
Cookhill, Alcester
Warwickshire
B49 5LJ

vintagedogbooks.com

ISBN No. 1-905124-86-4

Published by Read Country Books 2005


**British Library Cataloguing-in-Publication Data**
A catalogue record for this book is available
from the British Library.




**Read Country Books**
Home Farm
44 Evesham Road
Cookhill, Alcester
Warwickshire
B49 5LJ

# The Choice of a Gun

In the extensive B.S.A. factories the manufacture of rifles and guns on repetition machinery has been developed during the past 60 years to an extraordinary degree of accuracy. The parts of B.S.A. shot guns gauge to within limits of one thousandth of an inch. The materials used are specially selected by skilled metallurgists, and the gun as a whole was designed by skilled gun makers and sportsmen. The net result is great strength, perfect balance and "feel," the crispest of trigger pulls, and—by reason of the use of machines instead of expensive hand labour—phenominally low prices.

|  |  | £ | s. |
|---|---|---|---|
| B.S.A. Non-Ejector Gun, 12 bore | | 11 | 11 |
| „ Ejector „ „ | | 14 | 14 |
| „ Special Ejector Gun . | | 25 | 0 |
| „ Single Barrel, ·410-bore | | 3 | 15 |

*Illustrated booklets describing B.S.A. Guns and Rifles post free on request.*

# B·S·A
# SHOT GUNS

B.S.A. GUNS, LTD.
PROP. THE BIRMINGHAM

BIRMINGHAM, ENG.
SMALL ARMS CO., LTD.

2196)

*R. L. Illingworth.*

# SHOT-GUNS

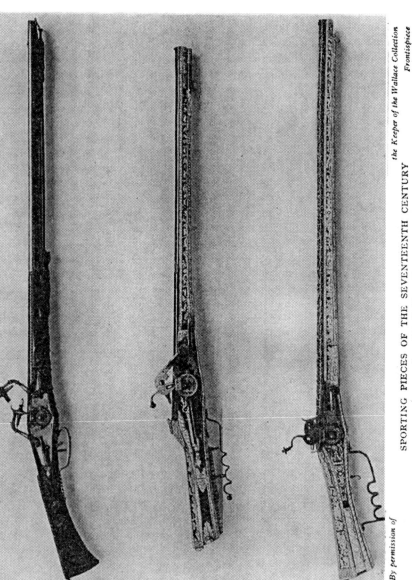

SPORTING PIECES OF THE SEVENTEENTH CENTURY

# SHOT - GUNS

## THEIR HISTORY
## AND DEVELOPMENT

BY

## MAJOR HUGH B. C. POLLARD
*Author of "Automatic Pistols," etc.*

LONDON
SIR ISAAC PITMAN & SONS, LTD.
PARKER STREET, KINGSWAY, W.C.2
BATH, MELBOURNE, TORONTO, NEW YORK
1923

PRINTED IN GREAT BRITAIN
AT THE PITMAN PRESS, BATH

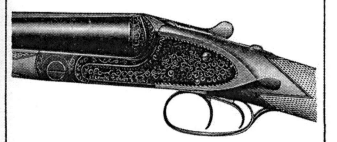

# PREFACE

THE modern shot-gun is essentially a standardized weapon which has reached a point in its evolution where it has settled down to certain definite types, and only minor improvements can be made. You may find a parallel to it in the bicycle, which evolved from a monstrosity of big and little wheels to the standard pneumatic-tyred diamond frame machine of to-day.

We have now reached a point where only a new major discovery—a new argon explosive, atomic power, or something of that kind—can effect any great change in our weapons. The breech-loader using smokeless powder is after all a weapon of only some thirty years' general usage, while its predecessor, the old flintlock muzzle-loader, endured without material change for close on two centuries.

A book of this kind dealing with a standard article cannot lay claim to any particular originality, but must honestly admit its indebtedness to all earlier writers. It is, however, a decade or more since any reliable handbook to the shot-gun appeared and many books are out of date or out of print. Post-war conditions of production and the influence of strained economic conditions have all led to changes which react alike on the gun trade and the sportsman. The perfection of handicraft which led to the works of the armourers and gunsmiths of the past being acclaimed as works of art is not easily to be found in the men of our own generation. Admittedly the present is a difficult time, but the future bears promise. In the history of the English gunmakers' art there have been times when

trade was at an even lower ebb and fine craftsmanship
at a hopeless discount, but there has always been a
renaissance and a revival.  Our national reputation
as the finest gunmakers in the world rests not on our
output of cheap goods meant to compete with rubbish
from Herstal, Eibar, or Suhl but on our "best"—our
first-class output.  There is nothing in the world to
compare with it for refinement, quality, efficiency, and
long life, and, above all, reliability and safety.

There is a curious proof to this very definite state-
ment and one that reflects not the opinion of an
individual but the accepted wisdom of a very wide
market.  The second-hand value of a good quality
English game gun in good condition shows *less depreci-
ation than any other commodity* with the exception of
gold or precious stones.  A good gun is an investment.

This little book will be widely circulated in the
United States and in the Dominions and Colonies.  In
its advertisement pages will be found the announce-
ments of the leading London gunmakers of to-day,
firms who can be relied on and whose names are in
themselves guarantees of first-class workmanship.

HUGH POLLARD.

1923.

# CONTENTS

# THE BURBERRY

## "The Coat for All Weathers"

THE man who wears **THE BURBERRY** has no need to worry about weather ; whatever befalls, his comfort and security are assured. No matter if it be a steady downpour or a light shower ; mild weather with odds on wet, or a keen north-east wind, **THE BURBERRY** is equally serviceable. Apart from its unrivalled protective powers, **THE BURBERRY** is faultlessly self-ventilating, cool on mild days and healthful on all. **THE BURBERRY** is so light in weight that it can be worn or carried without its weight being felt. Scientifically designed, it allows perfect freedom and is the ONE Overcoat in which it is possible to shoot without loss of form.

## BURBERRYS HAYMARKET S.W.1 LONDON

Bd. Malesherbes PARIS; & Agents in Provincial Towns

*Burberrys Ltd.*

# ILLUSTRATIONS

# THE
# HISTORY OF THE SHOT-GUN

## CHAPTER I

### INTRODUCTORY

FIREARMS were used for the purposes of sport practically as soon as the hand-gun developed out of its original form of a crude short cannon lashed to a wooden handle into the long gun type barrel, fitted with a mechanical device for the ignition of the charge.

The earliest arms were matchlocks, and the weapon consisted of a barrel and stock. At the side of the barrel was a small pan protected by a hinged cover. In the pan was deposited a small charge of powder. When this was lit the flash communicated from the pan through a narrow touch-hole with the body of the powder charge within the barrel. To fire this pan or priming charge a "match" was used. This match, or "mêche," consisted of a length of slow-burning saltpetre-impregnated rope. This was gripped by the jaws of a "serpentin" or "cock," and pressure on the trigger caused the pivoted serpentin to revolve on its axis and dip the burning end of the match into the powder in the priming pan.

As can be imagined, the matchlock was not an ideal sporting arm, for there was little possibility of surprising game while the lighted match smoked and smouldered all the time. Nevertheless the cumbrous

I

matchlock was used for sporting purposes, and even to this day is still used by native hunters in China and the native states of India.

The matchlock was followed by the wheel-lock. This device marked an enormous advance in the applicability of firearms to sport, for it dispensed with the tiresome ever-burning match, and substituted a mechanism which only produced the igniting flash when it was wanted. The firearm thus became a weapon of surprise no less than the bow. The wheel-lock was practically the same idea as the familiar little cigar lighters of to-day, where a milled wheel is spun round in contact with a " flint " and produces a stream of sparks which light a petrol wick. In the gun-lock it consisted of a wheel which was wound up by means of a separate detachable handle, or " spanner," against a powerful spring. The serrated edges of the wheel projected into the powder pan, and the cock or serpentin which had held the match was adapted to hold a flake of iron pyrites or flint in its jaws, and this was pressed into contact with the wheel in the pan. When the trigger was pressed the spring caused the wheel to buzz round, and the contact of pyrites and iron wheel produced a stream of sparks in the powder.

The wheel-lock remained the favourite sporting weapon until the period of King Charles I. Its use was mainly limited to sporting carbines and arquebuses and pistols, while the rank and file of the army still carried the simpler and cheaper matchlock, which was adequate as a military arm.

The wheel-lock was always a fairly expensive piece of work, and very beautiful and artistic weapons were made. A good many of these have been preserved

2

in the museums of to-day, but they are becoming increasingly rare and valuable. The earliest hand firearm in the armouries of the Tower of London is a matchlock harquebus of King Henry VIII, dated 1537. The wheel-lock, though said to have been invented at Nuremberg in 1515, is not represented by any dated specimen earlier than 1603, though five pieces attributed to the late sixteenth century are shown. That they were sporting weapons is clearly shown by the wonderful decoration and inlay, which show hunting scenes.

The first true shot-gun to occur in the collection is the " birding piece " of Prince Charles (Charles I), dated 1614, which is neither match nor wheel-lock, but a snap-haunce.

The snap-haunce lock is the forerunner of the true flintlock, but it represents a transitional stage between the wheel-lock and the standard form of flintlock, which was to endure without material change for well over a century. The snap-haunce appears to have been developed toward the end of the sixteenth century, and was made in England in 1585, while the standard flintlock did not come in till about 1630.

In both snap-haunce and flintlock the hammer carries a flint with which it delivers a blow on a steel anvil or frizzen, the sparks from which fall into the powder pan and fire the priming. In the earlier snap-haunces this steel is a separate member from the pan cover, which is moved back from the pan to uncover the priming powder by a delicate internal mechanism similar to that used in the wheel-lock. In the flintlock the steel and pan cover are one, and the impact of the flint throws back the pan cover. Snap-haunces, owing to the fact that they were made only for, say, a period

3

of fifty years, are extremely scarce, and any arms of this type are prodigiously valuable to collectors.

By 1660 the flintlock had become wellnigh universal as a standard lock, but wheel-lock carbines for deer-hunting were made in Europe as late as 1720.

The book of designs for gun engraving drawn by Jaquinet for the Parisian gunmakers of 1660 shows a gunmaker's workshop where current arms are represented in process of repair. Both wheel-locks and flintlocks are plainly drawn, and a long flintlock fowling-piece, with the wooden fore-end running almost to the muzzle of the barrel, is screwed in the vice for repairs.

The early shot-guns were for the most part single-barrelled, though double guns have been made even in wheel-lock times. The earliest double guns had the barrels arranged under and over instead of side by side, and had cumbrous double locks. There are many variants of this type, and a favourite device was to use only one hammer and revolve the barrels round a central spindle to present the second pan and steel to the hammer.

These double weapons were "freak" arms until about 1770, when the art of shooting flying game came into general vogue. Till then fowling-pieces had been long-barrelled single pieces, with the wooden fore-end continued to within a few inches of the muzzle.

As sportsmen began to shoot flying game a demand came for shorter, lighter, and more manageable arms, and the wooden fore-end was cut down to little more than its modern length, and the barrel shortened. The advantages of a quick second barrel became obvious, so the first double game guns appeared. In early specimens there is no rib joining the two barrels

4

beyond a short bridge or distance piece at intervals, and as the gunsmiths had not yet hit on the idea of flattening and trimming down the tubes at the breech, where they join one another side by side, the early double barrels were uncomfortably broad at the breech.

There are not many of these early pieces left to-day, for they were not beautiful enough to find a home in museums, and probably passed into the hands of keepers and farm hands as " old-fashioned," and so in process of time have disappeared.

The modern game gun varies but little in outline and balance from the form prescribed by Joseph Manton in the early nineteenth century and, indeed, the art of sporting shooting is almost a nineteenth century development, for in an extremely able book on guns, *An Essay on Shooting* (1791), we read " At this time we find that in France there are persons, who, when they fire, place the stock of the piece against the centre of the breast ; that in England many good sportsmen shoot with both eyes open at the instant of drawing the trigger, and that the Prussian settlers of Spitzbergen do not raise their piece to the shoulder, but place the butt end between their arms and their side, fixing the eye steadily on the object toward which they direct the barrel."

The celebrated Spanish barrels of this period were three to three and a half feet long, and usually of 22 or 24 bore. Bore is the same as calibre, but was gauged by the number of bullets to the pound. The old naming system still continues in use to-day, but the diameters are no longer exact to the lead ball proportions.

The best British makers toward the end of the

eighteenth century were Egg and Twigg, but they were rapidly surpassed by the genius Joseph Manton, who was born in 1764 and died bankrupt in 1835, after an amazing career in which expensive litigation absorbed all his profits.

Joe Manton guns are eagerly sought after by collectors of the present day, and his arms go right through the flintlock and transition period into the standard percussion double-barrel gun. The celebrated Colonel Hawker has nothing but praise for Joe Manton, whose art as a gunmaker made the colonel's achievements as a shot possible. In his *Instructions to Young Sportsmen* (the fourth edition of 1825), we find the double-barrelled flintlock shot-gun the established arm struggling hopelessly against the percussion system.

Manton revolutionized the sporting-gun world not so much with his exquisite flintlocks as with his percussion arms, and Manton's workmen founded gunmaking firms whose names are famous as existing concerns to-day. Purdey, Lancaster, Hussey, and Atkins are among the number. Manton's work shows not only an exquisite mechanical perfection, but a wonderful harmony of design. His guns handle completely differently from the clumsy arms of a few years earlier, and so evident were his successes that the other gunmakers had perforce to follow on the lines he laid down. His main improvements are the now familiar raised top-rib and the use of platinum in touch-holes, besides many detailed changes in breeching muzzle-loaders.

The outstanding firearms invention of the nineteenth century was the discovery of the percussion system for discharging firearms. It was not only an improvement on the existing flintlock system, but it was a radical

INTRODUCTORY

advance in ignition systems which later made breech-
loading and the invention of the modern cartridge
possible. All modern small arms owe their existence
to this discovery.

In 1807 the Rev. Alexander Forsyth, a Scotch
clergyman, patented the use of fulminating salts to
fire powder. In the early mechanisms the powder
was used loose or in pellets or enclosed in tubes, but
by 1820 it had found its normal standard application as
the familiar copper cap placed on a hollow nipple com-
municating with the powder chamber. The invention
of the cap is claimed by many, but it is probable that
it was simultaneously arrived at by many gunsmiths.
Manton for a long time stuck to his patent detonating
tube, but later adopted the cap system, and made his
finest weapons for it.

The percussion cap soon led inventors to think of
combining it with a charge of powder and shot so as
to provide a self-contained cartridge containing its
own means of ignition. As soon as this was evolved
the breech-loading principle, which had never been
satisfactory with loose powder and ball, because of
the escape of gas at the breech, became a practical
possibility.

In 1836 Lefaucheux brought out his pin-fire cartridge, in which a brass pin projected through the case
to the outside of the gun, where it could receive the
blow of the hammers. The other end of the pin was
centred in a vertically-positioned copper cap within
the cartridge. The effect of the cartridge was that
it expanded with its own gas pressure and automatically prevented any escape of gas round the breech.
This escape, which had been the great trouble with
non-cartridge loading breech-loaders of earlier type,

was in some cases enough to burn through a handkerchief tied round the breech, but the invention of the gas-tight cartridge completely did away with all objections to the breech-loading system.

The Lefaucheux gun was double-barrelled, pin-fire, and had the now familiar hinge action used in all modern shot-guns. By 1850 the breech-loader was creeping slowly into favour, and between 1850 and 1870 all kinds of different mechanisms and breech systems were devised. In most of these a double

FIG. 1

A LEFAUCHEUX TYPE PIN-FIRE BREECH-LOADER BY
JOSEPH LANG

motion of the lever for opening and closing was necessary, and the first snap-action gun, Needham's patent, appeared in 1862. A year previous to this Daw's central fire cartridge—the ordinary cartridge now in use—made its first appearance.

Between 1865 and 1870 the first hammerless sporting guns began to come in, and the Anson and Deeley hammerless gun, the simplest standard action ever devised and in general use to-day, was invented in 1875.

The modern shooter is so accustomed to the hammerless arm that it is difficult to think of the days of hammer guns, and still harder to realize what the muzzle-loading times were.

To-day two shots are fired, the breech opened, the

INTRODUCTORY

cartridges ejected, and the hammer mechanism all cocked by the simple process of opening and closing the gun. Our grandfathers, having fired two shots, had to pour the right charge of powder out of a flask into each barrel, ram down a wad on the top, then shot had to be poured in from another flask or belt, and this in turn had to have a top wad secured over it. The ramrod was then returned to place, the weapon lifted, and each hammer raised to half cock, the old caps removed, and new ones placed upon the nipples. Lastly, before firing each hammer had to be again raised to full cock.

In bitterly cold or wet weather, shooting with slippery, numbed fingers must have been a misery, and even under decent conditions the leisurely business of reloading and the general slowness of the cycle of little operations a trial to the temper.

With the progress of invention, the gun has become both easier and vastly quicker to use and, above all, very much safer. In the old days the careless sportsman had infinite chances to hurt himself or somebody else. Double charges were loaded into barrels, caps snapped and hung fire, powder flasks exploded, and people fired off their ramrods. To-day careless handling or an accidentally choked barrel are about the only possible causes of accident, and shooting is robbed of two-thirds of those dangers that made it a really dangerous sport in mid-Victorian days.

The last improvement of all was the ejector, a device which automatically throws out the discharged cartridges when the action is opened. This was the invention of Needham in 1874.

The ejector is in every way an improvement upon the ordinary extractor shot-gun, but adds to the cost

9

of the arm. Many good quality weapons are still made without ejectors, and the cartridges, though partly extracted by the mechanism, have to be withdrawn by hand. Lack of ejectors means such a loss of time with even the handiest and nimblest fingers that the extra cost can never be other than compensated for by the gain in speed and convenience.

These shot-guns of the nineteenth century were made for use with black powder, and not until smokeless powders were applied to use in shot cartridges in the eighties was there any great variation from the normal black powder standards used in muzzleloaders. The early smokeless powders were imperfectly understood and, as they gave higher breech and chamber pressures than black .powder, weak mechanisms and soft metals failed to stand up to the power, and accidents occurred.

The process of time has standardized smokeless powders, and they are now the only kind used, but it must be remembered that only the modern guns are designed for use with smokeless, and that it is dangerous to use smokeless cartridges in an old gun which has never been made for them.

All guns in which smokeless powder can be used are marked with the special nitro proof marks, which give the maximum charge that can be safely used in them. On arms proved with black powder there is nothing but the proof marks, and the words " nitro proof .. oz. maximum " are *not* applied. Sometimes very old guns by well-known makers are offered at extremely low prices ; in most cases purely because they are old black-powder arms and not proved for smokeless. Such weapons are usually valueless and obsolete, and may be extremely dangerous with modern cartridges.

# CHAPTER II

## THE SELECTION OF A GUN

THE choice of a gun depends on two main principles. Firstly, it is essential that the gun selected should be suitable for the particular kind of sport the purchaser has in mind. Secondly, the type of weapon required having been settled, the question of what quality or what standard of refinement is necessary must be determined according to the purchaser's purse or needs. The owner of a large Norfolk sporting estate, a young man about to go to Canada or Australia, and a shooting man about to take up wild-fowling, all need different kinds of gun if they are to be equipped with the weapon most suitable to their requirements.

So far as Great Britain is concerned, there is what may be called the standard game gun, which is suitable for all ordinary purposes with the exception of wild fowling. This is the double-barrelled 12-bore hammerless ejector gun, firing the ordinary British 2½-inch game cartridge. This type of arm is also made in hammerless non-ejector types, and in the cheaper grades hammer guns are still manufactured.

A gun which is simply needed for rabbiting, shore shooting, and kindred general casual work, does not need ejectors, which add to the expense and somewhat increase the delicacy of the weapon without conveying any material benefit so far as that type of shooting is concerned. For use in the ordinary shooting field, either for covert shooting or for partridge driving, the ejector gun is now indispensable. An ejector is a gun which when opened throws out or ejects the empty cartridge cases. Non-ejector guns are fitted with extractors, that is when opened they cause the cartridges to project out of the barrels so that they can be grasped by the fingers and withdrawn, but they do not " eject "—that is, shoot them out clear of the mechanism. The task of reloading an ejector gun can be accomplished in less than half the time needed for a non-ejector, and under modern game-shooting conditions this saving of time is extremely valuable, for birds may be driven over the guns in such swift succession that speed in re-loading is all-important.

The standard 12-bore hammerless ejector game gun can be obtained in many different grades from that of the " best " gun of a first-class London maker down to cheap low-quality productions from small provincial factories and country gunsmiths. A great deal of importance attaches to the selection of a first-class firm because the maker's name is in its way a guarantee of excellence, and the gun will always be worth a definite price in the second-hand market. A plain second-grade gun by a good maker is invariably worth more than the decorated " best " gun of a firm of little reputation, and only really good guns made by expert gunsmiths are satisfactory to their owners.

The wealthy man who goes in for a great deal of game-shooting buys his guns in pairs, and adds new pairs to his battery from time to time rather than have the old ones altered. Even more important folk have their guns made for them in threes or fours, but a pair is enough for the average need, and it is probable that 50 per cent of the people in the country who get only a moderate amount of shooting are content with just one gun.

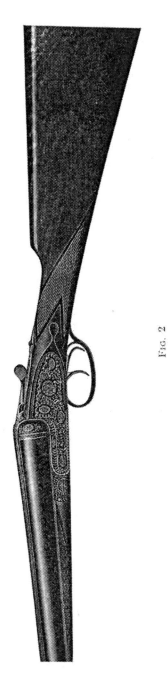

FIG. 2

BOSS'S DOUBLE-TRIGGER ORDINARY GUN

The difference between a "best" gun and other qualities seems at first sight to be disproportionate to the noticeable difference in price, and is best looked upon according to the depth of one's purse. If money is of little relative value compared to having the finest possible thing, in which all that is highest in craftsmanship, best in design, and exquisite in finish has been centred upon producing a perfect arm— then unhesitatingly purchase the best. If, on the other hand, twenty or thirty pounds extra represents an outlay that would only be justifiable if you were going to get a gun that would be definitely better in shooting quality or had some big definable advantage over the lower-priced arm, well then the difference is not worth the money to you.

The choice can be further determined according to what kind of shooting you propose to do and how much of it you are likely to get ; a "best" gun is not essential for a few days' rough shooting, and a good quality Anson and Deeley type of hammerless ejector by a first-class maker is a gun that can be borne in any company anywhere.

The "best" gun is usually made with side locks instead of the box action of the Anson and Deeley type. These locks make the arm more expensive, and in no way add to its efficiency, but they make it rather more delicate in balance, graceful in appearance, slenderer and more tapered at the action than can be achieved with the Anson and Deeley type. Except for this difference with the actions there is nothing to choose between a best side-lock gun and a best Anson and Deeley. The variation in price is entirely due to the extra cost of side-locks and the trouble of fitting them. For real hard usage and work

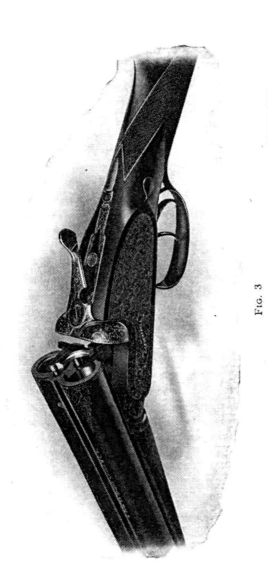

Fig. 3

A "BEST" QUALITY STANDARD 12-BORE HAMMERLESS EJECTOR SIDE LOCK
BY E. J. CHURCHILL

without constant attention and overhauling at the end of every season, the Anson and Deeley pattern is by far the best. It is almost invariably fitted to guns for overseas use, and is superior to side-lock guns of any other quality than " best."

The choice of a gunmaker is just as important as the choice of a gun, and it is absolutely essential that he should be a first-class man, not only with regard to the weapons that he supplies but also as a capable gun-fitter. Guns may be compared to cloth, they may be excellent—but unless cut and fitted by an expert the best cloth makes an unsatisfactory suit, and the best made gun is no good unless it fits its user.

The history of gunmaking is largely a record of famous individual gunmakers, and their success was due just as much to their knowledge of their art as to the excellent quality of the'r wares. Among London makers of the highest possible reputation are Purdey, Holland and Holland, Charles Lancaster, Boss, E J. Churchill, Woodward, and Lang.

The question of finish and engraving on a gun is one of individual taste, but even the finest gun in the world looks bare and mechanical without a little applied art. The engraving serves to hide lock-pins, screws, and junctions of breech and barrel, which otherwise look unsightly, and modern taste is increasingly in favour of such embellishments as really good engraving and even carving on the steel fences. Bad, scratchy, meaningless engraving is a sure sign of a cheap, bad gun, but good work, which costs money, is not necessarily the sign of a best gun, though seldom put upon a poor one.

Let us assume that a man has selected his gunmaker, decided how much money he is going to spend,

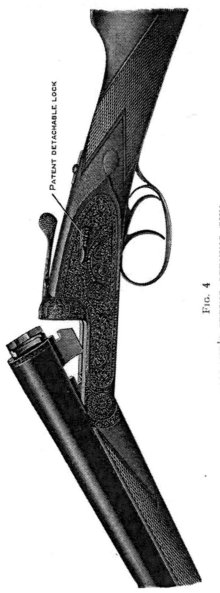

PATENT DETACHABLE LOCK

Fig. 4

HOLLAND'S SPRING OPENING GUN

and made up his mind what grade of gun he is going to buy. The next thing that he is called upon to decide is what particular performance he wants his gun to be capable of. Does he want it to shoot close at long ranges, or does he take his shots fairly near to, and so prefer an arm that scatters its charge over a wider circle ?

Gun barrels can be bored either to scatter or to concentrate the charge of shot, and guns are tested for their performance by an examination of the " pattern " that their standard load makes in a 30-inch circle at 40 yards  The standard charge is 1⅛ oz. of No. 6 shot, which is 306 pellets. A gun-bored true cylinder should put 40 per cent of these (122 pellets) into a 30-inch circle at 40 yards. With an " improved cylinder " the shooting is closer, 50 per cent (153 pellets) go in ; with " half choke," 60 per cent (184 pellets) ; with " full choke," 70 per cent (214 pellets).

Besides being able to put the requisite number of shot into the circle, it is important that these should be evenly arranged, leaving no bald spaces, for a close-shooting gun is of no value if it throws an uneven pattern with spaces in it, which would mean that game within the circle would yet escape the charge. The remainder of the pellets that are not within the circle are scattered round it and have the same killing power as those within the area. The problem is to decide what particular degree of close shooting is the best for each particular man.

On the average, the bulk of game is killed at much closer distances than 40 yards, and the average shot will do better with a gun that gives a wider pattern at close range—say, right-barrel cylinder, left half choke. This is particularly true of men who are rather

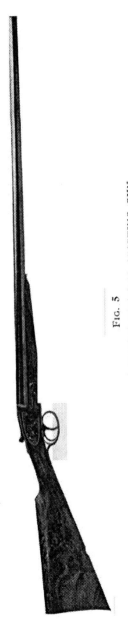

FIG. 5

PURDEY HAMMERLESS EJECTOR SPORTING GUN

short-sighted and fire quickly at comparatively close ranges rather than long ones, where they cannot see the bird clearly. Barrels an inch or two shorter than the normal are also often a great assistance to the short-sighted shot.

The man who is a good clean shot can afford to use guns with greater choke and concentration than the normal shooter, because he will be rewarded by being able to bring off long shots where the wider pattern of the cylinder might fail. With the full-length barrel, 28 in. long, the ordinary combination of cylinder right barrel and half or modified choke with the left is not as useful to the poor shot as a double cylinder.

If you know your shooting capacities, be frank with your gunmaker and tell him how you shoot. If you are not sure about them go down with him to a shooting ground and he will try out your capacities while fitting you with a " try-gun." This is a gun with a stock capable of minute adjustments for the standard gun measurements. It adjusts for bend—which is the distance from the top of the heel of the butt to the extension of a straight edge laid along the barrel, and also from the top of the " comb " or cheek piece of the stock to the same line.

The try-gun also adjusts for " length," which is from the fore-trigger to the heel, centre, and toe of the butt respectively, and for " cast off," which is the amount that the stock is out of centre with the barrels, in order that the latter should " come up " to the shoulder with the rib central to the line of vision.

The try-gun is not a magic solution of the fit problem by mechanical means, it is simply like being measured.

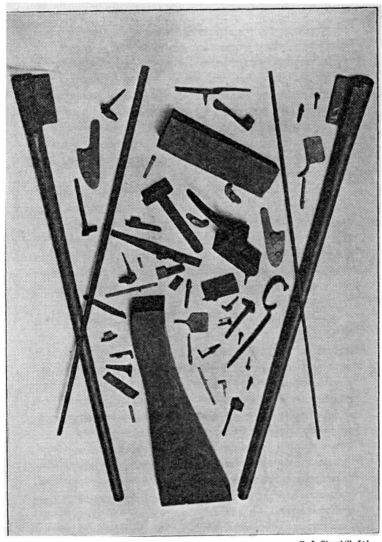

Fig. 6

THE RAW MATERIAL

# THE HISTORY OF THE SHOT-GUN

The fitting of a gun, like the fitting of a suit, is a second experience dependent upon the skill of the fitter. Thus, the slope or curve given to the butt to suit different shoulders is important. In the same way the heel of the butt may be cast off more or less than the toe, a long-armed man wants more length, and so on to infinite refinements. This is where the skill of the gunmaker comes in. The actual finishing touch is when the gun as made to fit the client is shot by the client on the shooting ground.

A good gun by a good maker is capable of a lifetime's use, provided that it is kept in good condition and treated fairly. A cheap gun may be an economy in the first instance, but comes off badly when the question of its lasting power is taken into account. The reason that good guns are costly is because a great deal of time and fine hand workmanship is put into them.

Factory-made guns, as turned out by the big Birmingham gun factories, are reliable, sound arms, but they lack that all-essential hand craftsmanship and *perfect fitting of every detail* that the skilled workmen of the good gunmakers put into their work, but they are also materially cheaper. It is only when the factory or part factory-made arm is put alongside the other that the real difference becomes manifest.

A " best " second-hand gun by a good Birmingham concern is as a rule worth £10 to £20 less than a similar London gun by a first-rate maker, a point of some importance when the financial side of gun selecting is considered.

In first-class craftsmanship the machine can never surpass the skilled workman. A modern gun is the product of many people's hands, for it is made piece

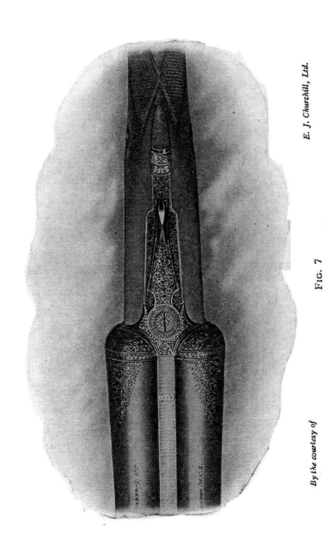

Fig. 7

THE FINISHED ARTICLE

by piece and process by process by men who do that particular job and no other.

The modern gun barrel is steel, for the old twist and Damascus barrels, so beautiful in their day, have

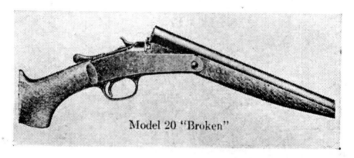

Model 20 "Broken"

Gun Taken Apart

By courtesy of                              London Armoury Co.
FIGS. 8 AND 9
WINCHESTER BREAKDOWN SHOT-GUN

yielded to the modern weldless tube of high tensile strength steel. Excellent as Damascus and various other welded barrels were for black powder, they did not stand the strain of nitro powders well unless made inconveniently heavy, and the improvements in steel soon made it possible to supply weldless steel tubes

24

SELECTION OF A GUN

both superior to the Damascus and built up barrels—
and at a far cheaper price.

The boring of the barrels, the joining together by
means of a rib, the filing of the action blocks, all these
are separate trades done by different men. The breech
action has as many specialists at work upon it. Locks
are the work of special gun-lock manufacturers;
" jointing," which is fitting the barrels to the action;
" fitting up," which is the making and fitting of the
action bolts; " filing," which is the shaping of the
action body—all these are different trades. Stocking,
screwing, polishing, blueing, and engraving are others.

So fine is the general quality of workmanship
required that a good modern gun can be considered
one of the finest works of skilled craftsmanship extant,
and certainly it is as good as the best products of the
past, despite the introduction of more mechanical and
machine tool processes and modern materials.

These points are worth considering when selecting
a gun, and it can be confidently asserted that the
" best " gun is the better value in terms of workmanship, material, and promise of life-long efficiency and
satisfaction.

25

# CHAPTER III

## GAME GUNS, WILD-FOWL GUNS, AND SMALL GUNS

THE foregoing considerations stated in the last chapter apply equally well to all types of gun, but it falls to many of us that though desirous of the best we must perforce, from economic reasons, be content with something a degree or two less than perfection.

In pre-war days the price of a " best " gun was sixty guineas, to-day the same gun costs at least eighty guineas, and if certain refinements such as " single-trigger " action and solid leather case, first quality accessories, etc., are added, the outfit may be taken to cost a round £100.

A good, sound, reliable Anson and Deeley action hammerless ejector gun, with case and equipment, can be purchased for approximately £30, and a plain B.S.A. hammerless shot-gun—an admirable weapon—as low as £11 11s.

Guns, unlike motor-cars, last one a lifetime, and there is nothing but first cost to be considered provided that they are scrupulously kept in condition and properly cleaned. There is, however, the second-hand market to be considered.

Good second-hand shot-guns by really good makers can be bought at moderate prices because they are slightly old-fashioned and have seen their best days. Provided these guns are proved for smokeless powder and are in good condition, they are good value, but unless a man has considerable knowledge of guns he should not buy second-hand arms without expert

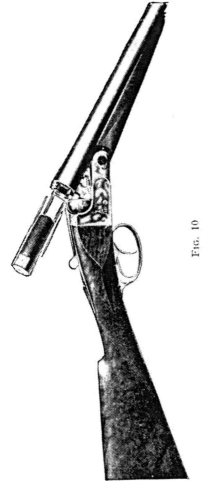

FIG. 10

THE CELEBRATED B.S.A. MACHINE-MADE GUN

advice, as it is extremely easy to be deceived. Most gunsmiths have a few good second-hand guns that they have taken in exchange or bought from the executors of deceased customers. Often these are old, but as good as when they were made. A man is always well advised to buy second-hand guns from a real gunmaker rather than through advertisements or pawnbrokers, as the " imitation second-hand gun " meant to catch the credulous is still a favourite device of the sharks. Guns with no name on them or guns bearing the names of unknown makers should never be purchased. All good guns are numbered, and, when there is any question about buying a gun, the prospective purchaser can always write to the original maker giving the number and asking for information about the original price and date of manufacture. I have never heard of any case where the makers objected to supply the requisite information in answer to an inquiry, but it should be borne in mind that the prices of good second-hand guns after the war may for a while exceed their original prices because of the change in purchasing power of the sovereign.

For Great Britain the normal all-purpose game gun is the 12-bore hammerless ejector double barrel, weighing from $6\frac{1}{4}$ to $6\frac{3}{4}$ lb. and having barrels of 30 in. or 28 in. American guns of this type are usually very heavy and cumbersome, weighing as a rule a full pound heavier than the British standard and lacking both grace and balance. All American 12-bores are bored for a slightly longer cartridge than the British $2\frac{1}{2}$ in. case. The American case is $2\frac{5}{8}$ in. long and American customers ordering guns made in this country should remember to specify that their guns

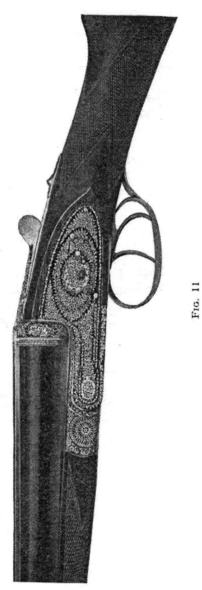

Fig. 11

LANCASTER'S LATEST MODEL OF BEST QUALITY HAMMERLESS EJECTOR SIDE LOCK GUN should be chambered for this slightly longer cartridge. The same rule applies to guns bought in this country for use in Canada where the American cartridges are in universal use.

In addition to the normal 12-bore there are guns of other bore or calibre, which have particular uses. In the large bore there are the wild-fowl guns of 4, 8, and 10 bore. All these are more or less special weapons built not for all-round shooting but for the particular needs of the wild-fowler. The latter needs a gun firing a heavy charge of big shot which will be effective at extreme ranges. The subject will be found more fully debated under the heading of ammunition and ballistics.

Eight bores are made both in single and double-barrelled arms, hammer and hammerless, and the double-eight was for long the standard wild-fowl gun. The 4-bore is seldom made other than as a single barrel for shoulder use, and is inconveniently large and powerful, the recoil being too much for most people. Double 4-bores and larger calibres up to 2 in. are used for punt guns, but these are abnormal weapons, beyond the scope of this handbook.

The up-to-date wild-fowler has largely abandoned these heavy gauge arms and has taken to special long-chambered 12-bores, capable of taking cases up to 3 in. long and handling charges of $1\frac{1}{4}$ oz. of shot. Experience has shown that greater efficiency is obtained by the use of a comparatively light gun weighing from $7\frac{1}{2}$ to $8\frac{1}{2}$ lb. than by adhering to a large-bore gun weighing several pounds heavier but only firing an additional $\frac{1}{2}$ oz. of shot. The special wild-fowling long-chambered 12-bores are, of course, unsuitable for ordinary game shooting because of their weight and

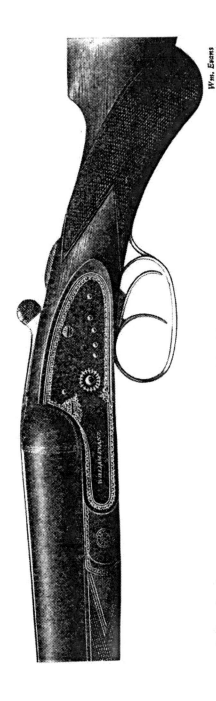

Fig. 12

SPECIAL WILD-FOWL "KYNOCH" 2¾" OR 3" CASE GUN

because they are, as a rule, very heavily choked and bored to give special close patterns at long ranges.

Between the ordinary game 12-bore and the wild-fowling piece comes the trap or pigeon gun, which is again an arm built for a particular purpose and not suitable for general use. The pigeon shot—that is to say the breaker of clay pigeons—requires a weapon bored to give the fullest possible efficiency of pattern at a certain known range. Pigeon guns are therefore built rather more heavily than game guns, $7\frac{1}{2}$ to $8\frac{1}{2}$ lb. as a rule, and take a $2\frac{3}{4}$ in. cartridge. The gunsmith exercises his skill to produce a barrel which will give a specially perfect pattern at the specified distance, 30, 35 or 40 yds., as the case may be, and pigeon and trap shots often have a special gun for each of their distances.

The small-bore game gun is more important than the bores greater than 12, for it is growing in popularity as an overseas arm for use in hot climates, where weight both of arms and ammunition must be reduced as far as possible. South America, China, and other markets are all now anxious to import the lighter calibres, for such game as is shot there rises within easy range and is as vulnerable with the lighter arms as with the more generally useful and more powerful 12.

The small-bore game gun of 16 or 20-bore is a lighter replica of its standard 12-bore brother, but it fires a smaller charge and is therefore not as efficient. A long and enthusiastic controversy has been waged by small-bore enthusiasts, who have striven to prove that the 16-bore is the equal of the 12, but as can be seen from the following table the

32

# GAME GUNS

comparative values of the standard charges show that the smaller guns can never be as effective as the larger.

| Bore. | Inch case. | Grs. powder. | Oz. shot. | No. of No. 6 Pellets. |
|---|---|---|---|---|
| 12 | 2¼ | 42 | 1 1/16 | 306 |
| 16 | 2½ | 36 | 7/8 | 238 |
| 20 | 2½ | 31 | 3/4 | 204 |
| ·410 | 2½ | 17 | 7/16 | 119 |

By using longer cartridges and heavier loads in the small bores a nearer approximation to the effect of the 12-bore can be attained, but in order to do this the very virtues that commend the small bore—lightness, balance and reduced recoil—are all sacrificed. A 16-bore can be loaded with long cartridges, but in order to do this the weight of the arm must be brought within a few ounces of the 12-bore weight if it is to be fired without giving more recoil than the standard 12. In addition the velocity of small-bore charges is less than the standard velocities of 12's.

Practically speaking, the 16 and 20-bore guns for the standard loads are excellent for use in hot countries or for boys, ladies, and elderly men who need a light gun with less recoil than the standard 12. A 16-bore weighs approximately 6 lb. compared to the normal 12 of 6¾ lb., a 20-bore 5½ lb.

Assuming that a 20-bore—the favourite small bore—is used, then the shooter saves 1¼ lb. or so of weight, but each shot that he fires has only two-thirds of the killing chances of the standard 12-bore, for he fires only 204 pellets instead of 306. This reduced number of shots cannot make as big a pattern as the

33

full charge, and therefore the number of killing chances is reduced.

So far as range is concerned, small bores are as effective as the 12 for all normal game shooting distances, but as they shoot fewer shot a considerably higher standard of personal skill is required if they are to perform well at the longer ranges.

The 20-bore is an ideal gun for ladies and boys of 14 or more, for it is light to handle, and if not made too light has no serious recoil. It is perfectly suitable for use at all game, and can be bought in all styles and qualities. The ammunition, too, is standard, and can be purchased anywhere though not quite as universal as the ordinary 12.

For quite young boys the weight of a 20-bore is rather too much, and the recoil heavier than they can bear without pain and bruising. Although a keen boy will stand up to it rather than forgo his shooting, the little ·410 double-barrelled shot-gun is much the best for youngsters under 14. There is no recoil to put them off and make them flinch from their shots, and the whole weight of the arm is not more than 4 lb. These little guns are cheap and made only in very medium qualities, but they are perfectly adequate to the service required of them, and will bowl over rabbits at 40 yds. The very fact that they have only one-third the chances of a full-grown gun means that the youngster has to shoot extremely straight in order to hit, and this early training in close marksmanship is the best foundation in the world for later success with the 20 and 12-bores.

A boy can be trained with a ·410 in the management of his gun in the field, in shooting etiquette, and above all in the scrupulous care of his own gun with regard

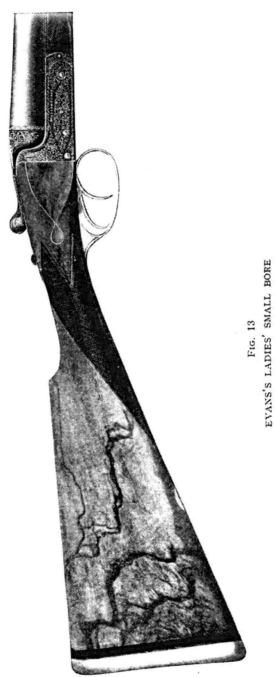

FIG. 13

EVANS'S LADIES' SMALL BORE

to cleaning. His attainment of success in regard to these matters should be made a condition of his promotion to the larger 20-bore, and this second weapon should be his first hammerless.

Thirty years ago the wrangle between the conservative adherents of the hammer gun and the progressive disciples of the hammerless was still in vigorous action. To-day there is no room for discussion, for the hammerless type is standard. With the hammer gun the lock for each barrel has to be cocked by hand in addition to the ordinary motion of opening the gun for re-loading. With the hammerless the simple opening or closing of the arm cocks both hammers automatically.

The gun is carried loaded and cocked, but a safety slide set on the top of the small of the butt prevents discharge while it is set to " safe," and is only normally thrown into the firing position when lifting the gun to the shoulder for a shot. In actual practice this is a perfectly safe system, but in the old hammer gun, when each lock cocked by hand, it was possible accidentally to discharge the arm if the hammer slipped from under the thumb while cocking, and further accident was possible from blows from external sources falling on the hammers. In other words, there are lots more chances for trouble with a hammer gun than with a hammerless—and as trouble in the shooting-field usually happens to anyone rather than the man handling the gun that goes off, the hammerless is the safest. The price is necessarily rather higher, but so is the speed with which the arm can be used, and this alone compensates for the excess, leaving the additional margin of safety as clear profit. According to tradition, boys start shooting with a hammer gun, but

# GAME GUNS

as soon as they are old enough to have a proper arm like a 20-bore, and shoot in company, this should be a hammerless model.

In the past there was room for discussion about the mechanism of the shot-gun. To-day it has steadied down to within such standard limits that beyond the choices between side-lock and Anson and Deeley actions, ejectors and non-ejectors, double or single trigger, there is little to say. All modern shot-guns have the lever on top of the action, the well-known " top-lever " fastening. Guns with levers at the side or under the guard are old-fashioned, though this latter action is still the best for heavy double rifles, and is still used on pigeon guns.

The locks and ejecting mechanisms of makers vary according to their own ideas. In some the weight of the falling barrels is used to cock the hammer and ejector springs, in others the closing of the barrels cocks the locks and ejectors, but, practically speaking, all the best guns of the best makers are as good as one another.

The lock mechanisms of shot-guns are peculiarly delicate pieces of work, and the less they are pried into the better. If anything does go wrong—a most unusual thing with any decent gun—the gunmaker is the only person to deal with it, for repairs or adjustments to a good gunlock are entirely beyond the amateur, however good a mechanic he may be. If a gun is well treated and properly cleaned and looked after, there is no reason whatever for trouble of any kind, and an annual visit to the maker is an almost absolute safeguard against the slightest bother.

A gun that gets hard use is bound to wear, and any signs of the slightest looseness or shake anywhere should be looked to at once. The wear usually shows itself as a slightly too easy action of the breech or, possibly, one trigger pulls harder or lighter than the other. These are matters for the gunmaker to adjust. In the same way a barrel sometimes gets a slight dent in it from a fall or knock. When this occurs it must go straight back to a gunmaker for the dent to be hammered out, and on no account must it be fired until repaired.

The most delicate parts of an ordinary gun are the ejectors. These vary in type, but are the same in system, that is to say they may be looked upon as separate locks, whose function is not to discharge a cartridge but to expel it from the chamber. These ejector locks are cocked when the gun is opened and closed for loading. When the trigger is pulled for either barrel the internal striker for that barrel falls and frees the ejector, so that when the gun is opened it flies out, throwing out the discharged case.

Ejectors have a considerable amount of work to do by comparison with their power; therefore it is of the utmost importance that they should be kept clean and well oiled.

The last refinement of the double-barrelled gun is the single trigger mechanism. This is not yet a standard fitment, but is growing steadily in popularity. In the ordinary gun right and left triggers are used for the respective barrels. This involves shifting the trigger-finger from one to the other between shots. With a single trigger two successive pulls on the one trigger discharge both barrels. The objection raised to their use is that when using a gun with a cylinder right barrel and a half-choked left, long shots are usually taken with the left barrel. With a single

FIG. 14

BOSS'S VERTICAL BARREL SINGLE-TRIGGER GUN

trigger either both barrels have to be discharged, or, if it is of a selective pattern and can be arranged so that one or other barrel can be fired at will, time is lost in setting it over from right to left, or vice-versa.

The earliest single triggers had other troubles as well, and shooters found them inclined to fire both barrels almost simultaneously. This was due to little understood reactions due to the effect of recoil causing the shooter to pull again on the trigger involuntarily. These troubles have now been successfully overcome, and the modern single-trigger is reliable. If a second-hand single-trigger is purchased it is most important to be sure that the trigger system on it is the one *now* used by the maker and not an early and unsuccessful experiment or one fitted to the existing gun by some other maker.

For the ordinary man the single-trigger is not an essential, but the additional cost is not high, and it is an improvement well worth having on any first-class gun or on, say, a pair of guns intended for grouse or partridge driving, where quick shooting is essential.

The latest type of double-barrel gun is a reversion to the oldest, for the first wheel-lock double-barrels were under and over's. The under and over gun is rather more convenient to handle as there is not such width to grip and it can be made rather lighter. As against it there is the fact that the placing of the ejector mechanism is rather more complicated, and that it has to be opened wider than the standard type to load. So far there is no actual standard under and over, and it is probable that the best and neatest mechanism for this new type of arm has yet to be evolved.

The future may, though I doubt it, see the

40

FIG. 15

LANG'S UNDER AND OVER GUN

supersession of the ordinary standard side-by-side double-barrel by the under and over type, but it must always be remembered that where the standard gun is the result of the concentrated experience of years, novel types have yet to get that hard crystallization of knowledge that comes only through extended use.

The trouble in the past has been the difficulty of securing the barrels to the breech sufficiently solidly to dispense with awkward top rib extensions. These top fastenings of the " doll's head," and various cross-bolting types have disappeared from most of the best guns of the ordinary double-barrel type and are usually only retained on specially powerful arms such as pigeon guns and ball and shot weapons. In the ordinary shot-gun, provided that it is thoroughly well made of sound materials, no top projection is needed, and its addition gives no additional strength to the action besides being a minor hindrance to quick loading. The barrels are held rigidly in place by the bottom lumps on them engaging with the solid body of the action where they are secured by the sliding locking levers moving in mortices in the action. The strain of firing falls on these lumps, tending to force them from the breech in a direction parallel with the barrel. On a cheap gun a top doll's head is a sure sign of indifferent material.

With the under and over the distance between the top barrel and the securing lumps was increased by the width of the second or under barrel. In order to prevent these actions working loose at the breech, top extensions of various kinds were used. The Woodward under and over dispenses with the ordinary lumps under the lower barrel in favour of side lumps on both

FIG. 16

WOODWARD'S PATENT UNDER AND OVER GUN

sides of the barrels, and further securing bolts passing through the face of the standing breech. This arrangement gives a mechanically sound joint much less in depth than the commoner systems, with the result that the gun is both stronger and much pleasanter to handle than many other under and over shot-guns.

The over and under type costs a few pounds more than the usual standard arm and is customarily made only in the best qualities.

Just before the war certain German firms were endeavouring to popularize their extremely unsatisfactory 12-bore under and over guns, which they were willing to export in a "white," unfinished state, for finishing by other makers. The wholesale price of these cheap and nasty implements was about £9, and they were catalogued as "in white, ready state, without German tests or other signs."

Continental shot-guns as a whole are so bad that a foreign proof mark is quite enough to scare off the least critical purchaser, hence the avoidance of " tests." Nevertheless, it is as well to beware of all guns unless they bear a reputable name, for under the existing laws these arms could have been proved in Great Britain with a British proof and sold with no mark to betray the country of origin.

# CHAPTER IV

REPEATING, AUTOMATIC, AND BALL AND SHOT-GUNS

THE British gun-making firms specialize in making the very best double-barrelled shot-guns in the world, and there is no other nation which can produce such first quality weapons. The French, Belgians, Germans, and Spanish all now export factory-made arms modelled on the distinctive English lines, but the performance of these guns is poor, and their life less than a quarter that of British. A casual examination does not disclose the weakness of these arms, and very often the external finish is deceptively good. The trouble lies mainly in soft, unsuitable material. The latter is easier to work in manufacture. As a result, foreign barrels of fairly good steel are often fitted to actions whose components are soft and unreliable. After a little use the whole " works loose," springs lose their resiliency, and the bents and scears wear hard or dangerously light. British arms, on the other hand, are made from specially selected material throughout.

The boring of foreign barrels is also extremely indifferent, and their shot-guns as a whole should be looked upon more as factory products for the export trade than as conscientiously manufactured weapons for sport. The foreign proof marks are also indicative of tests which are often less stringent than the British standard, and as a rule the patterns thrown even by good quality Continental arms are extremely indifferent.

American arms, on the other hand, are in a different class. The normal American shot-gun is a sound, reliable, but ponderous weapon. It is a factory product, and with, I believe, the exception of the Parker Gun Company, no concern in America hand-finishes its weapons. The American market demands a rather different weapon from the specialized perfected British game gun. They have different game conditions to face, and the purchaser's demand has been in the past a demand for a rough type of arm. The tendency of to-day appears to be in the direction of the more perfect British arms, but it is only recently that the American public have developed a keen sporting press, and begun to realize the necessity for conserving their game and placing their shooting on a higher grade of sportsmanship.

In the United States and Canada repeating or automatic shot-guns are used. The use of such arms for game shooting in Great Britain is not good form, for in this country shooting is for the sport rather than for the pot, but in some of the wild and undeveloped areas of the States and Canada such guns are permissible and popular.

The repeating and automatic shot-guns are among the best known of American inventions in firearms, and the principle originated in that country, one of the earliest of these arms being the Spencer repeater of 1886. Both repeating and automatic shot-guns are now made by the two great firms, the Winchester Repeating Arms Company and the Remington-U.M.C., and repeaters by the Stevens and Savage Companies. To understand their popularity and general success, it is essential that the ordinary American double-barrel gun should be seen and handled, and the comparative prices of American double-barrelled arms and repeaters compared.

A plain standard 12-bore repeater by any of the big

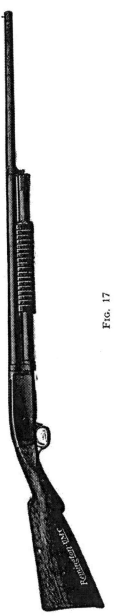

FIG. 17

THE REMINGTON REPEATER

firms cost before the war about £5 or £6, an automatic somewhere about £8 or £9. Any American machine-made double-barrel hammerless ejector of good make then cost about £17 to £20, and weighed no less than 8 lb.—usually more. Considering that a similar English factory gun weighs 7½ lb. at the most and then sold at about £12 to £15 retail, it seems curious that English guns of the ordinary trade qualities are not better known in the States, but as they have to compete against a very high tariff they are not widely handled.

The American of limited means naturally prefers an automatic or repeater arm which has some of the advantages of a reliable hammerless ejector and weighs about 7½ to 8 lb. to the cumbersome and heavy American shot-guns, which are more expensive to buy, heavier to carry, and no more efficient as killing weapons. At its price and of its kind, the American repeater or automatic was undoubtedly the best possible native value that he could get.

The American of moderate means who knows anything about guns buys a good English shot-gun when on a visit here, or if unable to come in person fills in a self-measurement form and sends it by post to a reliable English maker, accompanied at the same time by a few personal notes as to his height and general build, length of arm, breadth of shoulders, etc., and if possible a photograph or two. From these a good gunmaker can make a gun which, if not a perfect fit, is yet infinitely better than the standard ready-made factory-built American arms.

The question of the extra weight of a pound of gun seems a little matter on paper, but is all-important in the field. At the end of a long day every extra ounce

48

of weight tells, a tired man is slower to get his gun to the shoulder, and the lighter, better balanced arm is worth immeasurably more on the point of comfort alone.

The plainest grades of repeater and automatic shot-guns are, therefore, better value than most arms for the countries where they can be used, but, as the cost of finish, chequered stocks, and all small but essential refinements is inordinately high in the States,

Fig. 18
THE REMINGTON REPEATER

we find that a Winchester automatic shot-gun with a picked stock with a little chequering cost pre-war £17, while a pigeon-grade model, 1911, with a little engraving and decent stocks, is at least £37 to £40. For a pound or two more it is perfectly possible to get a good *pair* of English guns or one excellent one.

Repeaters are usually made with a tubular cartridge container under the barrel. Round this fits a movable wooden fore-end slide, and the arm is operated with a " trombone " action, the slide being pushed backwards and forwards to cock, eject, and re-load. This mechanism can be worked extremely quickly, and though two shots cannot be fired as swiftly as with a double barrel, the third and fourth are speedier than re-loading even an ejector. On the other hand, a shooter using a repeater loses more time in re-loading, and in point of speed a shot using two or more hammerless ejectors and having gun loaders to re-load for him and hand him the guns, surpasses both repeaters and automatics.

The model 1912 Winchester hammerless repeating shot-gun is made in 12, 16, and 20 bores to take six cartridges, and weighs from $7\frac{1}{4}$ lb. The arm has a detachable barrel, and can be furnished with additional barrels, bored cylinder, or modified choke. As issued, the guns are usually full choke and shoot too closely, but any barrel can be had on application. An earlier hammer model of 1897 is made in 12-bore and 16-bore only, and a 10-bore underlever duck gun is also manufactured, this latter weighing $8\frac{3}{4}$ lb.

The Remington model No. 10 is a 12-bore, 6-shot repeater, and can be had with a barrel of 26, 28, 30, and 32 in., according to preference choke, modified choke, or cylinder. The barrel detaches easily from the action, and the empty cases eject downwards instead of sideways, so that there is no chance of powder residue or cases being blown back into the shooter's face by the wind—a very material advantage, as " blow-back " or powder residue is extremely irritating to the eyes, and many a good shot has been spoilt by it.

The Stevens company makes repeating shot-guns in 12 and 16 bores, and also a particularly pleasant lightweight 20-bore repeater at a low price.

There is little to choose between the guns of all these makers so far as reliability, shooting powers, and general efficiency are concerned. So far as shape,

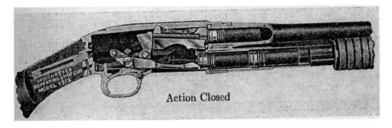

Action Closed

Fig. 19

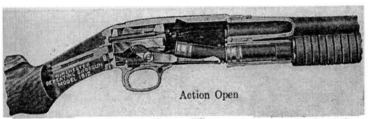

Action Open

*By the courtesy of*                                   *the London Armoury Co.*

Fig. 20

WINCHESTER REPEATING SHOT-GUN

balance, and easy handling, I consider the Remington far and away the best of all the repeaters of 12- or 16-bore. The little Stevens '20 is the pick of the small-bore arms. I have not yet seen the new Savage repeater, but all arms made by the Savage Company are as a rule excellent.

In automatic shot-guns there are the Winchester, Remington, and the Norwegian Sjogren arms to be compared. Only the Winchester and the Remington

FIG. 21
WINCHESTER HAMMERLESS REPEATING SHOT-GUN
Gun Taken Apart

need be taken into consideration. This latter arm is the type known as the Browning or F.N. automatic shot-gun, and is also manufactured in Europe as the Browning. It holds four cartridges in the magazine and one in the chamber, and is automatic in its action. That is to say the arm is cocked, loaded, and cleared of its empty case by the recoil of the preceding discharge, and all that has to be done by the shooter is the pressing of the trigger. The arm is made in a take-down in 12-bore only by the Remington firm, but was made as a 16-bore on the Continent. Its action is reliable and sound. Weight about $7\frac{3}{4}$ lb.

52

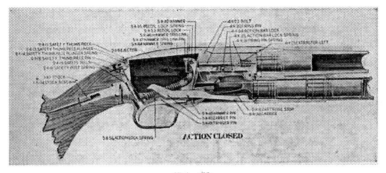

FIG. 22

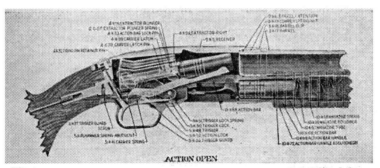

By the courtesy of                                          J. G. Rollins & Sons

FIG. 23

THE SAVAGE SHOT-GUN

The Winchester self-loading shot-gun model, 1911, is another type of recoil-operated automatic 12-bore gun, weighing about 7¾ lb., and it is slightly handier and rather more pleasant to fire than the Browning or Remington models. It has the same magazine capacity—four in the magazine and one in the chamber—is take-down, and can be fitted with differently bored barrels. The full choke model makes a good arm for wild-duck and shore shooting, but re-stocking to suit a particular customer is a difficult task, as the internal mechanisms reach far down into the wood of the stock.

Practically considered, the best trombone-action repeater is better than any of the automatics and far pleasanter to shoot with. Both repeaters and automatics are noisy in action, and despite their weight the recoil is more noticeable than with a standard double barrel. With automatics the recoil is far more severe than with repeaters. Although sound in design and construction, the multiplicity of small and complicated parts does not make for great reliability or long life, and when it is out of order new parts have to be obtained from the factory, as repair is usually too difficult for the local gunmaker.

Nevertheless these arms have a wide vogue in the United States, and to a certain extent upon the Continent, and can be considered reliable and dependable within their limits. Future developments of the system may greatly improve the type of weapon, but for general purposes these arms cannot yet be reckoned as equal to the standard double shot-gun and are never likely to supersede it.

As a general rule it can be asserted that combination arms designed to fulfil two or more functions are inferior to the normal arm for both. It is possible to combine the shot-gun with the rifle in many different ways, but the resulting weapon is not so good as a proper shot-gun and not so good as a proper rifle. The best combination arm is the 12- or 16-bore " ball and shot-gun," which is a rather heavy double-barrelled shot-gun, the barrels of which are very lightly rifled in order that it may be used for shooting a heavy conical bore bullet at ranges up to 150 yds.

The well-known Paradox gun of Holland & Holland is possibly the best known of these, but all makers can supply weapons of the ball and shot-gun type. The ordinary shot-gun with cylinder barrels will shoot round ball accurately to about 60 yds.

If the barrels are lightly rifled towards the muzzle or throughout their length they will fire shot with fair ordinary patterns at 40 yds., and will make a 6-inch group with ball at 120 yds.

The ball and shot-gun is a favourite weapon for the colonies, as it combines in one arm the qualities of a well-balanced shot-gun and a powerful double rifle. Such a gun costs about the same as a good shot-gun, according to whether it is hammer, hammerless, or hammerless ejector, and it weighs about $7\frac{1}{4}$ lb.

A good deal of attention has been paid to the problem of making good ball and shot-guns with ranges up to 300 yds. This has been achieved by increasing the charge of nitro powder and increasing the bullet length so as to get a light projectile of higher ballistic efficiency than the ordinary Paradox bullet.

The Westley Richards' " Explora " gun, 12-bore, weight 7 lb. 2 oz., will make a group $9\frac{1}{2}$ by $7\frac{1}{2}$ in. at 200 yds., and their " Fauneta," a 20-bore ball and shot-gun, carrying a special 290 grain capped bullet, weighs only $6\frac{1}{2}$ lb., and is good up to 250 yds. The

smaller " Fauneta," 28-bore, ball and shot-gun, weighs
5¾ lb., and has a bullet range of 300 to 400 yds., with
a muzzle velocity of 1,660 ft. a second, giving a
flat enough trajectory to make adjustments of sight
between 100 and 150 yds. unnecessary.

As a shot-gun it accomplishes all that a 28-bore
can be expected to, and is an ideal all-purpose gun to
carry in countries where a brace of birds for the pot
or a medium-range shot at buck may be two consecutive
shots.

Ball and shot-guns are better than either guns with
one rifle barrel joined to a shot barrel, or the rather
heavy three-barrelled gun affected by Continental
sportsmen. The double-barrel combination is usually
made with a 16-bore shot barrel and a rifle barrel for
·450 or ·400 cordite. As the rifle calibre decreases, so
it becomes necessary to fit a smaller shot barrel to
retain proportion, and 20 or 28 bores are usually cou-
pled with the ·303, ·318, and ·365 calibres. Under and
over actions of this principle with the rifle barrel
underneath afford a wider range of combination, and a
small-bore rifle barrel can be used with a 12- or 16-bore
shot barrel.

Three-barrelled guns with one rifle barrel underneath
are sometimes made to order, but even the best of
these are cumbersome and weighty, lacking the all-
essential shot-gun balance that makes the double
rifle, the shot-gun, or the ball and shot-gun a success.

The drawback to all these variations of gun and
rifle is that the double arm is really only a single of
each kind. Two kinds of ammunition have to be
carried, but even with the three barrel only two-shot
cartridges can be discharged, and the alternative use
of the arm as a rifle is as a single loader. The shooting

56

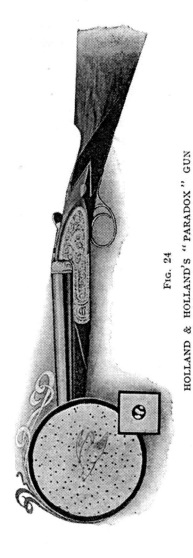

FIG. 24

HOLLAND & HOLLAND'S "PARADOX" GUN

of these combinations is not particularly precise, and the very need for keeping their weights down to normal limits means that they are considerably frailer than the normal double rifle, and much more likely to get out of alignment from a fall.

For sporting purposes the ball and shot-gun can certainly be recommended as a good reserve weapon with which to supplement a rifle battery. Such an arm is useful in India for jungle shooting, and is a good "second weapon" for emergency use to be carried by an attendant. On the other hand, the combination rifle barrel and shot-gun arms, either double- or three-barrelled, are not much use.

# CHAPTER V

## THE SHOT-GUN CARTRIDGE

HOWEVER good a gun may be, it is of little use unless the cartridges with which it is loaded are of the best possible quality and give an even standard performance. This is so little realized by shooters that it is no uncommon thing to see a man who is scrupulously particular about having an absolutely perfect arm, using cheap and variable ammunition with the natural disappointing consequences.

Modern cartridges are the outcome of endless experiment and research, and the great makers vie with one another in producing ammunition that can be depended upon to give absolutely even results. Imperfectly loaded cartridges are of extremely rare occurrence with factory-made ammunition, and the normal variation of load is kept within such extremely fine limits as to be practically negligible, so far as the shooting powers of the cartridges themselves are concerned.

All that has been said with regard to getting good guns and rifles by reputable makers applies with equal force to cartridges. Unknown and, in particular, cheap foreign made brands of cartridges should be avoided at all costs. Those loaded by good gunmakers in cases bearing their name, and the standard brands of Messrs. Curtis and Harvey, Kynock, or Eley, all of which firms are now in the group known as Nobels Explosives, Ltd., which can be bought anywhere, can be relied upon. Bargain cartridges and unknown imported powders and cases cannot. In the States the ammunition of the Remington-U.M.C., the Winchester R. A. Co., and other well-known makers can be relied on for use in English or American arms of good quality. The difference in price between the best and the lower grades of cartridges is so slight that it is always worth while buying the best, and to any user of an expensive gun the use of cheap cartridges is a " penny wise, pound foolish " policy.

The cartridge consists of a brass or paper case containing four components—the cap which ignites the charge, the explosive which propels the shot, the wadding necessary to confine the powder gases, and lastly the shot.

When the striker hits the cap this detonates, igniting the powder, which burns or explodes, giving off many thousand times its own volume of gas in a fraction of a second. This gas seeks to escape by the path of the least resistance, and as the breech and sides of the case are confined by the steel walls of the gun the wads and shot furnish the easiest path, and these are driven by the gas up the barrel.

Any variation of case, cap, powder, shot or wads will produce a different performance, therefore the cartridge-maker takes the greatest possible care to standardize not only the cartridge case and the proportions of powder, shot and wadding for the various bores, but all details of loading including the cap and the precise degree of " turnover " given to the lip of the case to hold the contents in place.

Shot-gun cartridges are made of a tube of paper with a brass and paper base. In the better quality cases the brass of the base extends externally over the powder chamber, and as a general rule the better the quality of the case the more brass it shows. A similar effect is produced in some cases by extending an internal thimble of metal into the powder chamber, which achieves the same effect of reinforcing and waterproofing the vital part of the cartridge.

A variation of the ordinary cartridge is the solid drawn brass cartridge case known as the " Perfect." These are used only in guns specially chambered for them, as the internal diameter of a " Perfect " case of 12-bore external dimension is much more than the internal diameter of the ordinary paper case, being practically a 10-bore load. Full brass-covered cases for ordinary guns have a paper lining which projects at the end and can thus be readily distinguished from the special " Perfects," which are only for wild-fowl guns.

The best quality paper cases are waterproof and little affected by normal damp, though even the best cartridges cannot be expected to stand a prolonged soaking without swelling. The cheaper paper cases are not properly waterproof, therefore their contents are affected by even moderate damp, and, as the amount of moisture in powders affects their shooting qualities, no regularity of performance can be expected.

Rain on cheap non-waterproof cartridges causes the paper tube to swell or blister. In shooting, cartridges may get wet particularly from rain running down the muzzles of the barrels. With cheap cases the expansion may be so great that difficulty is experienced in ejecting wet empties after firing, so one or both barrels may be rendered temporarily useless till the obdurate case is drawn out with an extractor or forced out with a straight hazel twig cut from the nearest cover. Good waterproof cartridges with plenty of brass on them will stand any weather and almost

61

any climate. For excessive tropical damp heat full brass-covered cases should always be used.

The cap or primer of a cartridge is vitally important, for upon minor variations in the behaviour of the cap depends the whole effect of the powder. In order to fire the cap properly the striker of the gun must be just the right length, not too sharp and not too blunt, and it must deliver a correct blow, not too weak nor too powerful. If the gun mechanism is good there is little likelihood of trouble with the cartridge caps, and with modern cartridges nine out of ten misfires occur through a gun rather than a cartridge fault. Out of thousands and thousands of rounds fired I can remember only a few odd cases of misfires, and it is to all intents and purposes a trouble that has been entirely overcome. The shape of the anvil inside the cap, the position and area of the flash holes, and the amount and degree of strength of the fulminate compound are all factors that have been most carefully studied by ammunition makers. The various nitro powders used require a cap very slightly different from the others if the best results are to be obtained, therefore when loading cartridges it is always as well to load A's cases with A's powders instead of B's, for each maker caps his cases to suit his own powders rather than other people's.

Sporting powders of the present day are the true types of smokeless powder, black powder having almost entirely disappeared except for wild-fowl guns. These smokeless or nitro powders are of three entirely distinct kinds, according to the amount required to produce effects in a shot-gun equivalent to the standard. The standard accepted for modern smokeless powder is designed to prevent excessive and dangerous breech pressures, and was worked out by the *Field* newspaper in order to establish a standard for gun-makers, ammunition-makers and sportsmen. Breech pressure is not to exceed 3 tons to the square inch, and the shot velocity over 20 yds. is a mean velocity of 1,100 ft. a second.

Guns are built to be used with cartridges giving this maximum, though they are, of course, proved with vastly more powerful charges. The standard, however, gives a normal point to work to, and the cartridge makers try to produce the best possible ammunition giving high shot velocities with low breech pressures and reduced recoil.

The first class of smokeless powder is known as "bulk smokeless," that is to say it occupies approximately the same space in the case as the normal load of 84 grains of black powder.

Bulk nitros are lighter than black and are loaded by measure, 42 grains of bulk nitro equalling the force of, and taking as much space as, 84 grains of black.

Bulk nitro powders are such brands as "Amberite," "Schultze," and the Kynoch "K.S."

The second kind of smokeless powder is called "Thirty-three-grain nitro," and is more concentrated than the bulk powders. The standard load is 33 grains, whence the name. Typical powders of this type are Diamond Smokeless, E.C. No. 3, K.S.G., "Lightning Schultze," etc.

The third class are condensed nitros, such as "Ballistite," "Neonite," and the Cordite and Axite powders used in rifles. These latter are not used in shot-guns, and Ballistite is loaded in special charges and special cases by the makers. These powders are termed dense nitros.

The function of the wads in a cartridge is to act as a gas check and prevent the powder gases blowing through the shot charge. The quality of wadding used in cartridges makes very sensible differences in their performance, and it is essential that it should be well fitting, firm, and elastic, and not liable to blow to pieces in the gun. The lowest wad set directly on top of the powder is a thin grease-proof card wad, usually black on one side. This prevents grease from the thick felt wad spoiling the powder pellets.

Next comes the felt wad which acts as an elastic gas check. This contains a certain amount of grease which reinforces its elasticity, and not only waterproofs the cartridge, but helps to lubricate the barrel and prevent leading. On top of the felt is another thin card wad, not necessarily waterproof, and, indeed, not essential except to fill up the case so that an excessive turnover is not required. Lastly, on top of the shot comes a thin card wad whose function is simply to retain the shot. This bears on it a printed numeral giving the size of the shot with which the cartridge is loaded. In American cartridges two thin felts in place of one thick one are more usually loaded.

As a general rule, diminishing the thickness of wadding between powder and shot causes greater spreading of the charge. In the same way shot can be made to scatter by putting one or two thin card wads between layers of shot and reducing the thickness of the felt wad by half, using another half felt as a top wad over the shot.

Shot is made in all sizes, from dust shot to big pellets, weighing four to the ounce. In order to give good results shot must be perfectly round, even in size, hard, and well polished. Oval pellets

# THE SHOT-GUN CARTRIDGE

or soft pellets deformed by the pressure of the powder gases lose both accuracy and range, and in flight deformed or light pellets tail off behind the main body of the charge so that the whole charge does not reach the target at the same instant. Thus if a mixed charge of No. 4 and No. 8 pellets were shot at a distant flying bird the lighter pellets would reach it an appreciable time after the heavier ones, and the bird might pass unscathed through the gap between the two varieties.

Shot sizes as turned out by the makers vary slightly with regard to the number of pellets to the ounce. In the same way, English and American shot standards are different; for instance English No. 6 is 270 pellets to the ounce, American No. 6, 218, and continental sizes are all in the wildest confusion. When ordering cartridges abroad, the only thing to do is to specify not the size of the shot but the number of pellets to the ounce. Here, again, you may be up against the decimal system and the local gunmaker may not know what an ounce is, therefore it is always wise to take a sample cartridge or two which can be copied, for even in countries which prohibit the importation of foreign ammunition one or two cartridges can be easily smuggled through in the pockets of clothes. The Continental shot sizes are now specified in millimetres according to their diameter.

The standard gun is made to place 40 per cent of any normal charge of any sized shot in a 30 in. circle at 40 yds with cylinder boring. As the barrel is increasingly choked the percentage rises to 70 per cent.

As most game is shot at 20 to 30 yds. the excessive concentration of the full-choke is too much for the

65

average shot, as, though the close pattern within the 30 in. circle is excellent, the larger killing circle or general spread of the shot charge is too much reduced.

In order to get the maximum efficiency out of a cartridge one needs the maximum number of killing chances, therefore the more pellets the better. If large pellets are used the number of killing chances are reduced, therefore it is obviously best to select the smallest size that will maintain sufficient velocity to have good penetration at ordinary killing ranges. Modern practice is all in favour of small shot, for it is now realized that even shot as heavy as No. 4 does not penetrate the well-armoured parts of a bird, and that the fatal shots are those which strike the softer comparatively unprotected vitals and nerve centres. For this purpose No. 7 is quite as efficient as No. 4—and as at any given range any given gun puts the same percentage of shots, irrespective of size, into the same area thus delivering the same weight of lead, the use of No. 7 gives twice the number of killing chances of No. 4.

Shooting men are by instinct conservative, and perfectly groundless and mythical traditions handed down from the flint-lock period still linger. Despite the theoretical value of No. 7 shot, the average cartridge firm supplies about 60 per cent of its ammunition loaded with No. 5, for there is a permanent demand for it as a good all-round size. Many shooters use No. 4 for all purposes, and point to the fact that they do well with it as evidence of its being the best. The probability is that the effect of windage on light shot is such that loss of power and range is experienced in rough weather.

No really efficient method of penetration testing

66

has yet been devised. The old way was to fire at a " Petitt pad," a pad of forty sheets of compressed brown paper. This answers well for rough and ready work, but as the paper varies in penetrability with dry and damp weather, and as its thicknesses are variable through inequalities of manufacture, it is of little use for accurate standardization work. The later instrument known as the Field Force gauge was also inadequate to the purpose. Nevertheless the sportsman can carry out rough and ready experiments sufficient to satisfy himself as to the relative penetrative values of small or large shot by the simple process of shooting at copies of old magazines, or any handy form of pads of the same kinds of paper. These should be hung from wires rather than supported against a firm background, and though the results are of no real scientific value they are useful for the comparison of different charges in one's own gun.

Penetration and pattern tests show the ordinary two dimensional effect of a charge in height and width of spread, but they do not show the *length* of the charge in flight. This will be further referred to in the following chapter.

Despite the fact that a gun can make a good pattern, the stringing effect or lag of a shot charge means that only about 40 per cent of that pattern can be counted as effective, as the slower tail pellets cannot be relied upon. In game shooting it is vastly more important that cartridges should be uniform than that they should show high but variable velocities. The higher the velocity the less allowance is needed for crossing birds, but if the velocity is variable you cannot estimate correctly—a factor which explains why a man will shoot better with one familiar make of cartridge than others containing a different powder. A change to a slower powder may make all the difference, for if one's normal allowance with a quick powder is just right for getting a bird with the full head of the charge, the slower powder allows the bird to move faster with the result that the shots go too far back. Conversely a change to a quicker powder may mean that you shoot too much in front and that the bird only flies into the tail of the charge.

It is just as important to get used to one's choice of a particular cartridge and powder as it is to get used to one's gun. In the normal way a good average shot can shoot fairly well with any cartridges and even a borrowed gun, but for clean efficient shooting, and all the little points that go to make up style, it is best to work out the load that suits you best and always adhere to it.

The danger of burst barrels has become very much less of late years, thanks to the improvements both in the manufacture of high grade steel tubes and more largely to the improvements in cartridges and cartridge loading. When the powder pressure is increased by some abnormal strain to a pressure greater than the barrels can bear, a burst is bound to occur. Any obstruction in the barrels at a distance from the cartridge will cause a burst or a bulge. Snow in the muzzles is a frequent cause of accident; mud or earth or wads from a previously defective cartridge have precisely similar effects.

The utmost care should always be exercised, and after passing through a snow-laden cover or a fall on slippery turf, the barrels should always be looked through to make sure that there is nothing lodged in them.

# THE SHOT-GUN CARTRIDGE

Another cause of burst is sometimes found with bad cartridges. One case may have only a little powder in it, and this only strong enough to blow the shot and wads part of the way up the barrel. A similar effect is caused by only the cap and no powder being in the cartridge. These faults do not occur when good cartridges by good makers are used. Very old cartridges with smokeless powders, cartridges that have been exposed for some time to tropical climates, and cartridges that have been badly wetted and imperfectly dried—all of these are liable to behave abnormally in shot-guns owing to changes occurring in the quality of the explosive. As a general rule all such ammunition should be destroyed, as it is liable to give dangerously high pressures. Unfortunately, it is often assumed that any such accidents weaken the nature of the cartridge and it is given to the gardener to shoot rats with. As he probably uses it in a rickety old black-powder gun the risk of accident is vastly increased.

The most dangerous form of burst is caused by a 20-bore cartridge getting accidentally mixed with the 12 bores. This will lodge in the cone and produce a double burst. It is a wise rule never to keep a 20-bore gun in a gun room where there is a battery of 12 bores. If a small bore is needed a 16-bore or a 28 should be chosen.

In the old days sportsmen loaded their own cartridges, and even re-loaded their empties. To-day cartridge loading is gradually being left less and less to the gunmaker and more to the big factories, for smokeless powder is extremely variable in its properties as compared with the old reliable black powder. Smokeless powders of to-day are not loaded according to standard formulae. In the same standard cartridge by the same maker it is easy to find variations of several grains in the powder load in cartridges made at different times. The reason for this is that each big batch of powder gives a rather different result to its predecessor. The pressure may be high or low within certain limits, but the charge is not loaded by weight or by bulk measurement, but each batch of powder is tested to find out the precise amount of that particular batch of powder necessary to give the standard result. Factory-loaded cartridges are therefore made from actual tests, not from standard formulae.

The hand-loaded cartridge is made up under conditions which allow room for every sort of error, and any kind of blunder may pass without notice. In the factory-loaded cartridge the whole reputation of the manufacturing firm depends upon their avoidance of errors, and their machinery is intentionally designed to prevent any error occurring. Every batch of powder is tested for velocity, pressure, recoil, ignition, and damp and heat tests. The component cases, caps, wads, and shot are all carefully tested, and the cartridge is completed by machinery that throws out any defective parts, and cannot proceed to subsequent operations unless the previous ones have been completed. In addition to this automatic check during manufacture, the completed cartridges are continuously sampled and tested.

Under normal conditions the *good* gunmaker loads cartridges that perform as well as factory-loaded ones, but the hand-loaded cartridges of the " rule-of-thumb " casual country gunshop are nowhere near as good or as reliable.

# THE SHOT-GUN CARTRIDGE

In selecting cartridges the points to be remembered are the following—

1. The best cases are the best value.

2. A quick 33-grain powder is preferable to the bulk slower-burning grades.

3. Large shot have a higher velocity than small shot, but at the sacrifice of a disproportionate number of " hitting chances."

4. The light 1-oz. load is sometimes preferable for a heavy day to the $1\frac{1}{8}$ or $1\frac{1}{16}$ in. as it gives a higher velocity and less recoil, the latter a consideration to sportsmen feeling their advancing years.

5. The harder the shot the less drop in velocity due to deformation of pellets; therefore use chilled shot.

6. Bulk for bulk small shot give a rather higher recoil than large, therefore with small sizes a 1-oz. shot load is preferable.

# CHAPTER VI

## BALLISTICS

THE subject of ballistics is a difficult one, for, in spite of the years of research work and careful observation and experiment which have been devoted to firearms, we still can only deduce approximate formulae from the recorded results of what does happen. In the matter of arms of precision, such as rifles, an enormous amount of work has been done, and the results are available in the official text-book of small arms. The scientific study of shot-gun results has, however, been in the main the private work of gun and ammunition firms, and the results are not so accessible. Most authorities, though, agree that the good modern shot-gun with suitable ammunition develops about 80 per cent of its theoretical 100 per cent efficiency.

The layman dreams of a high velocity shot-gun with an effective range of some 75 yds., and of a powder so quick that no " allowance " need be calculated for crossing birds. At present with a standard weight of gun under 7 lb. and a limit of 3 tons breech pressure, no such gun or cartridge can be built. We may expect little improvements in powder and components, small improvements in barrel-boring which may advance us a point or two in efficiency, but in point of fact the efficiency of the shot-gun is limited by the curious behaviour of a column of shot as distinct from a bullet.

We find that for a given charge of shot any increase of muzzle velocity over a certain speed in feet per second means a gain in energy, but only at the expense of pattern. The theoretical end we desire to attain

# BALLISTICS

is a far higher shot velocity without any sacrifice of the pattern or percentage of accurate killing hits which can be placed within the 30 in. circle at 40 yds. Let us examine the behaviour of a shot charge and the various obstacles it encounters.

As has been stated, the barrel-borer is able to bore a standard gun barrel either

" True cylinder " in which 40% of the pellets are within the 30 in. circle at 40 yds.
" Improved cylinder " in which 50%    ,,    ,,    ,,    ,,
" Half-choke "    ,,    60%    ,,    ,,    ,,    ,,
" Full-choke "    ,,    70%    ,,    :,    ,,    ,,

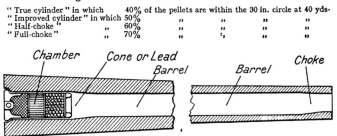

Chamber — Cone or Lead — Barrel — Barrel — Choke

DIAGRAM 1

DIAGRAMMATIC SECTION OF SHOT-GUN BARREL

A true cylinder is a barrel in which the diameter of the bore is the same throughout. That is to say from the chamber mouth or cone forward there is no constriction and the sides of the tube are truly parallel.

A barrel consists of a tube bored with several diameters. First comes the chamber to accommodate the cartridge, for the internal diameter of the cartridge is rather more than that of the barrel itself. Then comes the cone or lead which reduces the diameter of the chamber to that of the barrel and enables the charge and wads to pass through this cone or funnel into the length of the barrel proper. The main length of the barrel will thence be approximately cylindrical until the choke is reached. The choke is a constriction of the diameter of the barrel a few inches from

73

the muzzle, and within certain limits the severity of this constriction governs the pattern.

The principle of choke-boring dates from the eighties, and was a British discovery, but exact scientific knowledge of its functioning is still vague, and the laws governing its performance unascertained. All we can say is that chokes bored to certain dimensions ascertained by trial and error experiment give certain results.

When we consider the performance of a shot charge in a barrel, we must banish from our minds any previous ideas based on the performance of solid projectiles in rifles, and realize once and for all that a shot charge is not a solid but something much more like a fluid. Thus, if we press the top of a solid lead plunger sliding inside a tube it transmits the pressure direct in one line to whatever is beneath it, and exerts no pressure on the sides of the tube.

A similar amount of pressure applied to water would exert its influence in each and every direction equally, and the sides of the containing tube would be subject to pressure equally with the base.

A column of small shot substituted for the solid lead plunger or the water behaves in a manner which is between the two, but more like a liquid than a solid, and it is due to this factor that so far all attempts to increase velocity have broken down because of the equivalent increase in the scattering of the body of the charge after it leaves the muzzle of the gun.

The standard cartridge consists of the powder charge, the wads (whose function is to prevent the gases of the explosion rushing past into the shot charge, thus wasting energy and upsetting the formation of the shot column), and lastly the charge of shot itself.

74

# BALLISTICS

There is, however, another important item, and that is the crimp or turnover which secures the top wad in position over the shot and keeps all the components in place. Too much or too little turnover makes a big difference to the behaviour of the cartridge. In the old black powder days this factor was not so important, for with black powder the explosion

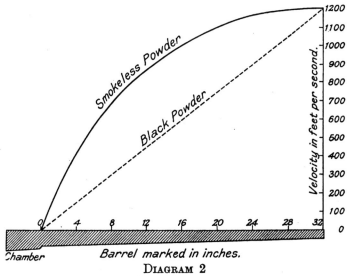

Chamber        Barrel marked in inches.

DIAGRAM 2

was gradual, so that the velocity of the shot charge increased almost evenly as the charge moved along the barrel. With smokeless powders, on the other hand, the initial development of velocity is very much more speedy.

Thus, from the diagram it can be seen that a charge propelled by black powder has only obtained a velocity of 100 ft. per sec. in travelling the first 4 in. of barrel, but that where smokeless powder is used the charge

75

obtains a velocity of over 300 ft. per sec. in the same distance.

There is also the factor of breech pressure to be considered. The powder, when ignited, gives off an increasing volume of gas, and the charge moving comparatively slowly along the barrel to begin with, only leaves a certain amount of space to accommodate this gas. It is a peculiarity of smokeless powder that the higher the compression the greater the rate of propagation of combustion. In other words, the greater the pressure the faster it develops more gas, adding to the pressure. In practice the wad and shot column exert such a resistance while gaining velocity over the first few inches of barrel distance that two-thirds of the maximum pressure is developed at the mouth of the chamber or cone, and the full pressure comes to its height between 7 in. and 9 in. from the breech. As the load moves along the barrel the available space for gas expansion is increased at a velocity exceeding that of the development of gas by the powder, and both the pressure and the rate of burning of the remainder of the powder charge drop.

This quality of the gas development, or rate of combustion of smokeless powder varying with the increase or decrease of pressure, accounts for the radical differences between black and smokeless powder shown in Diagram 2. So far as black powder is concerned, it has a quicker rate of ignition than smokeless, and develops its highest pressure within 6 in. of the breech, but it burns at the same rate all the way.

The practical results of these peculiarities are that gun barrels have to be made heavy enough and strong enough at the breech to resist these high local pressures, but the thickness of the barrel walls can be

# BALLISTICS

decreased toward the muzzle in proportion to the drop
in the pressure curve. In the same way it is clear
that though long 32-in. barrels were essential in the
black powder gun because the length was necessary
to ensure the complete combustion of the powder and
obtain the full 1,150 ft. per sec. velocity, the length of
barrel of a smokeless powder gun can be reduced to
22 in. without any material loss of shot velocity,
though to do this with a black powder charge would
mean a loss of 350 ft. per sec.

To return to the cartridge, it can now be clearly
seen that any factors which increase the resistance of
the load to the powder gases exert an immediate and
possibly dangerous effect on breech pressure, and in
any case disturb the harmonious relation of velocity
on which normal patterns depend. Thus in practice
we find that too deep a turnover is associated with an
unpleasant recoil and a sketchy scattered pattern.

Another and far more dangerous state of affairs
occurs when a cartridge ⅛ in. too long is used in
chambers meant only for the normal case. Such a
cartridge will fit nicely when loaded, but when it is
fired the turnover expands and constricts the cone so
that the whole shot and wad column has to be forced
by the gas through an aperture much narrower than
is customary ; not infrequently a burst or a broken
action results from this.

Apart from these possible errors of undue turnover,
etc., the cone or lead from the chamber to the barrel
is a very important factor in itself. In theory, the
cartridge, when fired, should open out and completely
fill the chamber, leaving the load to emerge into the
barrel, which should be but slightly less in diameter
than the internal bore of the cartridge case. Old guns

were made with an almost square-faced chamber end and no cone, but in practice this was not found effective for the sharp angle tilted the wads sideways and there was loss of gas pressure.

The function of the cone is to receive the shot and wad column and lead it compressed to a gas-tight fit into the barrel. A bad cone will tend to tilt wads sideways and allow the gases to expand through the charge, and too tight a cone will unduly increase gas pressure and add to the deformation of the shot.

The inside diameter of a fired case averages ·74, and a cylinder of this width has to be compressed into ·729, the diameter of the barrel, through the funnel of the cone.

In other words, the initial effort of the gases has to overcome the frictional resistance of the wads and shot column in the case, to overcome the inertia of the load, and to force the load through the cone into the barrel. The effect of firing the charge is that, in the first instance, the wad and shot column is compressed and expanded laterally by the first forward movement of the wads. The turnover then yields and the compacted mass of shot is squeezed forward into the cone. The mass of shot, however, behave more like a liquid than a solid, and some of the energy transmitted to the base of the column is transmitted as pressure to the barrel wall. The shot deform under pressure and the resistance factor of the load increases abnormally.

The conditions of stress which exist in the shot charge driving its passage through the cone and up the barrel, are not yet clearly ascertained, but it appears that the little understood factor of *adhesion* plays no small part. The shot charge theoretically consists of a cylinder of small spheres, but in practice this becomes

BALLISTICS

deformed into a cylinder of small uneven bodies with
multiple planes and surfaces in contact with one
another and with the barrel wall. It is one of the
peculiar properties of the mechanics of adhesion that
surfaces which will slide or rotate in relation to one
another when under light pressure become incapable
of this motion under heavy pressure. In other words,
the lower layers of the shot charge are so much under
pressure that they are impacted and solid, while far less
pressure is transmitted to the centre and topmost shot
layers of the charge.

The outside pellets of the cylinder are in pressure
contact with the barrel wall, and that this pressure is
intense is shown by the familiar longitudinal streaks
of " leading " that one observes in a barrel after use.
The deformation of the pellets in the barrel under
pressure can be illustrated by firing a shot charge into
a swimming bath and recovering the result. These
will show that without deformation from impact with
any object outside the gun no less than 30 per cent of
the pellets are deformed during their passage up the
barrel. This factor of deformation is very important,
as inaccuracy of flight and irregularity of pattern is
largely due to it.

We know from experience that in a cylinder bore the
spread of the charge is far wider than with a choke,
and we know that the stresses within the body of the
shot charge are such as to induce it to expand outwards
from its axis toward its circumference. What, then,
is the action of the choke ?

Let us presume that in a cylinder bore the top and
middle layers of the shot charge are under less stress
than the base. On emerging from the muzzle the
restraint of the barrel walls is lost and the charge is

free to resolve its stresses as it can. If the lateral or peripheral stresses bear a relationship to the forward acting stress set up by the pressure of gas on the base of the column, the tendency would be for the lower layers of pellets to spread further when released from confinement than the less impacted top layers.

The choke, which consists of a second cone or kindred constriction of the barrel diameter set a few inches from the muzzle, acts as a mechanical "shaker-up" of the moving shot column, and to a large extent offsets the tendency to lateral expansion and reduces the tendency to spread by resolving this outward tending force, the sloping shoulder or cone of the choke giving the peripheral pellets an inward rather than an outward tendency.

It is also probable that the general shake-up produced, when the shot column meets the choke, not only compresses and lengthens the column but also breaks down the impacted mass of pellets toward the base of the charge, and upsets the existing adhesion stresses.

In practice it is found that only a certain degree of choke can be obtained, and that reduction of the barrel diameter of ·729 to less than ·684 means that once again the pattern begins to become patchy and irregular, and shoots in groups and clumps of shot.

The effect of a degree of choke, i.e. the change from improved cylinder to modified choke, or from modified to full choke, is a gain of 5 yds. range for each degree. That is to say the pattern of an improved cylinder at 30 yds. would be the same as that of a modified choke at 35 or a full choke at 40.

The choke effect is not, of course, produced without some additional damage to pellets and a slight though practically negligible retardation of velocity. It is the damage to pellets which is the factor which actually counts, and for that reason chilled shot, which resists deformation better than soft lead, is to be preferred. As range increases the damaged shot either tail off or fly in more erratic paths. With the ordinary game gun used at normal ranges the average good pattern is enough for most people, but the wild-fowler who shoots at longer ranges is insistent in his demand for a special high velocity type of shot-gun free from many of the minor blemishes of the game gun. He contends, and with justice, that a loss of some 40 per cent deformed pellets is too high an average for efficiency at his work.

The wild-fowl guns most in vogue are very carefully bored, with no sharp cone or lead in front of the chamber but a very long gradually constricting funnel instead. The choke, on the other hand, is very full, and heavy charges of powder and shot are used.

In the game gun the ammunition maker relies on the presence of a certain amount of cone resistance, and allows for it, marketing ammunition whose powder actually needs this resistance in order to develop its normal efficiency. He has, be it remembered, to meet normal general demands with a universally suitable cartridge, and this is no easy task for guns vary very much in capacity, and very slight alteration makes a great deal of difference to the performance of the same ammunition.

The wild-fowler, on the other hand, is seeking for a special arm, and recently the chamberless gun—one in which the barrel diameter and the external size of the cartridge are equal, has been learnedly debated, and various old styles of boring used in muzzle-loading days have been resuscitated and adapted to smokeless powder uses. As matters stand " progressive " types of powder, that is to say powders whose grains have been devised to continue developing energy even when pressure falls, are used for rifle ammunition, but so far no satisfactory shot-gun powder of the kind has been produced in this country though the American Dupont Company have been trying out a special super-powder of this type. With such a powder and devices, or improvements in barrel-boring designed to diminish the deformation of pellets, it may be possible to attain a higher standard of shot velocity without loss of pattern, but it is doubtful if such an arm will show any greater efficiency in the hands of the ordinary sportsman than the weapons of to-day whose close shooting powers are very near to the limit of ordinary human marksmanship.

In the actual testing of ammunition a special gun, known as the " Field " proof gun, is used. It is quite unlike a sporting gun and looks more like a small cannon. It is equipped with crusher gauges at a point within the chamber and further along the barrel, 6 in. from the face of the breech, and has electrical contact equipment for the chronographical measurement of shot velocities. It is free to swing on its supporting wires and its backward movement indicates a comparative standard of recoil as measured by inches. Nine-and-a-half inches is the ordinary standard for the usual game cartridge.

An average normal cartridge should not develop breech pressures in excess of the 3 ton standard, though pressure up to $3\frac{1}{2}$ or 4 tons is not unusual with heavy loads and long shot columns.

The velocity of the charge may be taken at any

point, but the standard mean velocity is assessed on the difference between muzzle velocity and the velocity of the charge at 20 yds. The standard or normal is now 1,100 ft. per second.

The test of a normal game cartridge is usually carried out with the shot charges of $1\frac{1}{8}$, $1\frac{1}{16}$, and 1 oz., and the average result would be tabulated as follows—

| POWDER. | SHOT. | PRESSURE. Tons per sq. in. | RECOIL. Inches of travel. | VELOCITY, over 20 yds., ft. per sec. |
|---|---|---|---|---|
| 33 grains | $1\frac{1}{8}$ oz. shot | 3·35 | 10 | 1·085 |
| | $1\frac{1}{16}$ ,, | 3·2 | 9·4 | 1·095 |
| | 1 ,, | 3 | 9 | 1·105 |

The proof gun is also equipped with contacts to enable velocities to be taken at any point within the barrel, so that a most careful examination can be made of the behaviour of any charge or any new powder submitted for test. These internal ballistics are, however, seldom sought except in the case of samples varying very much from standard.

A sportsman who has reason to doubt the efficiency or reliability of cartridges he has purchased, should send a sample dozen to the Sporting Editor of the *Field* or *Country Life* with a request that they should be tested. The examination is carried out in the proof gun, and in addition to the record of pressure, recoil, and mean shot velocity, a report is made on the standard pattern made by the shot charge. This, however, only represents a standard, and in order to be perfectly certain about the behaviour of any particular ammunition or load, the cartridges should be fired for pattern from the actual gun used by the shooter.

The seemingly inexplicable missed shot may be due to the bird passing through an " open space " in the pellets of the pattern, or it may be that a " cartwheel " pattern has occurred. This is not a rare phenomenon but occurs about once to every ten or a dozen cartridges fired. A " cartwheel " is a pattern in which the centre 30-in. circle is more or less empty, and the charge is fairly equally distributed round the periphery of the circle so that the whole is like a ring. The cause is not known, but it is thought to be due to a perfectly-centred wad pushing its way through the body of the charge and dispersing the pellets with radial direction as it leaves the muzzle of the gun.

For ammunition tests " cartwheel " patterns are always ignored as " no shots."

On the other hand, it is not generally realized to what an extent the " stringing " of the charge permits chances of escape. The familiar " pattern " is, after all, only a two-dimensional record, and does not indicate the depth or stringing out of the comet-like body of the charge. Tests have been carried out at different ranges, taking not only average pattern records, but also by firing at a target consisting of a long strip or roll of paper moving laterally at a known speed. From this roll it is possible to gather an impression of the length of the flying charge and the extent to which it has strung out during its flight.

At 20 yds. the charge from a 12-bore choke will spread to give a 20 in. group, but in length the charge will have strung out to a column some $3\frac{1}{2}$ ft. long. A cylinder barrel giving a good pattern within the 30-in. circle at the same range will show the column extended to 5½ ft.

As the velocity of a shot charge drops rapidly the stringing effect becomes far more marked as range extends. Experiment shows that at 40 yds. the distance from the leading to the hindmost pellets may be a full 10 yds. The normal procession of the charge shows that the head of the flight consists of 5 per cent of the total effective pattern composed of pellets of particularly high velocity closely followed by a thicker layer of 25 per cent, which is followed by another mass of 20 per cent. This first half of the charge represents its efficiency and occupies the first 3 yds. of the total string of 10 yds. of depth. The balance, or tail, consists mainly of deformed pellets of irregular distribution and rapidly decreasing velocity with little killing value.

A bird crossing the 3-ft. killing circle at the rate of 40 miles per hour, at 40 yds. range, occupies the danger zone only for ·05 of a second. As it takes ·138 of a second for the first shot to reach the circle and the last shot may be full ·05 of a second later in reaching it, the bird may easily be clear of the area before the last pellet arrives. Further, the progress of the bird across the area may quite possibly be such that by luck it never is in a position to be hit vitally by any pellet and is always in a " blank space " in the pattern, although succeeding pellets arriving later may fill in that space on a fixed target so that the pattern would look as if it were impossible for a bird to escape.

The loss of velocity of a shot charge varies with the size of the shot, heavy shot maintaining velocity far longer than light.

The following instances show the approximate loss for an equivalent charge.

VELOCITY IN FEET A SECOND

| CHARGE.<br>3 drams powder. | 10 yds. | 20 yds. | 30 yds. | 35 yds. | 40 yds. | 45 yds. | 50 yds. | 55 yds. | 60 yds. |
|---|---|---|---|---|---|---|---|---|---|
| 1¼ oz. No. 1 shot | 1,140 | 1,090 | 1,000 | 960 | 935 | 910 | 890 | 860 | 825 |
| 1¼ oz. No. 5 shot | 1,035 | 1,045 | 970 | 915 | 875 | 835 | 790 | 740 | 670 |
| 1¼ oz. No. 10 shot | 1,040 | 940 | 830 | 775 | 710 | 550 | 465 | 425 | 370 |

In practice, heavy shot not less than No. 1, and usually B.B., or even mould shot, is used for long-range work against tough swiftly-flying birds, such as duck or geese. The 700 ft. a sec. velocity appears to indicate the lower limit of the reliable killing speed of shot, and the loss of penetration and energy below this level is extremely noticeable.

Just as the reported speed of people's motor-cars varies with the optimism of the owners, so one hears a good deal of loose talk concerning the ranges at which game is killed by long shots. Now and then an occasional long shot is brought off, more by hazard than design, and the bird falls apparently vertically from the heavens. Actually it curls over in a neat curve, and the shooter, proud of his prowess, paces the distance from shooting point, not to where the bird was shot but to where it fell. Thus it can be seen that a favourable slant of wind may appear to increase killing range in the most formidable manner.

The amateur, or sportsman, who has painstakingly read through this chapter may not have acquired deep technical knowledge, but he will at least have obtained some general grasp of the ballistic capabilities of the normal game cartridge, and understand the difficulties which confront the gunsmith or the ammunition-maker who strives to improve any one quality of a cartridge without achieving a loss of efficiency on one of the others.

Heresies still persist and the average keeper still believes in " putting a pinch more powder in," and there are still country gunmakers who crimp their cartridges precious hard because their farming customers believe that a stiff recoil is an index of a good strong shooting charge, but in the main popular knowledge is increasing and old myths dating from black powder days are being forgotten.

# CHAPTER VII

## THE GUNROOM, ACCESSORIES, AND DRESS

WOMEN can be certain to take good care of a grand piano ; it has the best room in the house, is attended by a skilled tuner, and, even in the darkest days of war when coal-rationing was a serious problem, fires would be lighted to prevent damp from affecting the instrument. A pair of good guns cost more than a grand piano and deserve just as much care, yet unless care is taken they are liable to be relegated to the garage or the boxroom, and left neglected till the next season comes round.

A complete room sacred to guns and their accessories is not essential, but a good lock-up, glass-fronted gun cabinet, where they can be kept under their owner's eye, is manifestly the best way of being sure that they have not been stowed in some damp and unsuitable place. The gun cabinet should be in the owner's study or library, or some room that is in constant use, not damp, and maintained at an equable temperature, for damp is extremely bad both for guns and cartridges.

These cabinets are usually made in the same shape as bookcases, the lower part forming a cupboard, or being fitted with drawers for accessories and cartridges.

More or less standard patterns of gun cabinet may be purchased at the big shops or stores, but these are rather gloomy stained or fumed oak objects lined with depressing green baize. A much better cabinet, made preferably in good mahogany and lined with a polished wood veneer, can be made by any decent cabinet-maker. This should be carefully designed to go with

88

the other furniture of the room, and should be perfectly dustproof and of sufficient height to take the over-all measurement of your longest gun or rifle.

The alternative to the full-length cabinet is a glass-fronted hanging cupboard fitted with leather-covered hooks to support the arms, but this is neither so convenient nor so sightly as the full-length cabinet.

In a man's room, a well-fitted gun cabinet can be made much more decorative than is usually supposed. The blued-steel barrels, the grey of the actions, and the gleaming polish of the walnut stocks all harmonize well with well-filled bookshelves and a few good prints.

Personally I love to have my guns round me, for they are great reminders of pleasant memories—of satisfactory rights and lefts, and that wonderful long shot at a single sky-high duck.

Guns, to get the best value out of them, need a master's eye ; the right man to clean a gun is the owner, for, though the keeper or the footman may do it well enough, they lack that personal interest in the task that makes it a pleasure. To this end, then, proper cleaning materials should be kept handy in the cabinet.

The requisites for shot-gun cleaning are simple and few, but they must be kept clean and they must be kept together. First comes the cleaning rod—a stout wooden rod joined by a screw ferrule in the middle for ease in packing into the gun-case and fitted with a brass tip into which screw a brass jag, a wire scratch-brush, and a woollen mop. In addition to these, a short-handled round bristle brush for cleaning out the chamber, a narrow but stout bristle brush on twisted wire such as is sold for cleaning pistols, and a small toothbrush are also useful. These small brushes are for cleaning out recesses in the action and getting at

89

difficult places where a rub over with a rag is not sufficient.

For cleaning material, tow to wrap round the jag, and soft patches made preferably from old woollen underclothing, flannelette or something similar, are necessary; oil, such as Price's Rangoon, or the even better " Three-in-One," and in addition a bottle of paraffin, a bottle of linseed oil, a tube of vaseline, and a few cleaning rags or dusters.

Tools are seldom needed, but the cabinet should contain two or three screwdrivers of good quality with specially fine edges, so that if a screw is drawn it can be done without marking or burring the head of the screw. A pair of flat-nosed pin pliers and one or two short lengths of silver steel of different wire gauges to serve as punches, are also useful.

When a gun is brought in from shooting it should be wiped over with a rag and the barrels just brushed through. It can then stand for a while till you have changed and had a bath, and have leisure to attend to it.

To clean a gun, remove the fore end and detach the barrels from the stock. Proceed to clean the barrels first. Wrap a pledget of tow round the brass jag and oil it; with this, swab out each barrel two or three times, always finishing by pulling the rod right through the barrels in one sweep. Next clean out the chambers with the bristle brush, clean and vaseline the outside of the barrels, paying particular attention to underneath the ejector or extractor and the guides in which they move in the barrel lumps. Next wrap a clean soft wool patch round the jag and clean the barrels thoroughly until a clean patch goes right through without the slightest mark of grease or dirt.

Hold the barrels up to the light and examine carefully for any traces of leading, which are with difficulty discernible as dull-coloured streaks on the polished steel of the barrels. If these are detected, the scratch-brush, which should always be made of *brass*, not steel, wire, must be oiled and the barrels thoroughly scoured, but the scratch-brush should be used as seldom as possible.

The danger of leading is that powder residue collects underneath it and corrodes the barrels, causing rust and pitting after they have been put away. With average care this should never occur in a shot-gun.

Having ascertained that the barrels are perfectly clean, put a few drops of oil on to the mop and pull it through each barrel. The mop must never be used in a foul barrel and must be kept sacred to this final oiling.

The bed, joint, and action of the breech should now be cleaned with the bristle brush and thoroughly wiped over with an oily rag. All moving parts should be lightly lubricated with the finest non-clogging gun oil such as " Three-in-One." Too much oil cannot hurt the metal parts of a gun though it may clog them; on the other hand, too little may cause pounds worth of damage.

The stock should be wiped clean with a soft woollen rag, and occasionally rubbed over with a few drops of linseed oil. Linseed oil must be used only for the woodwork, never for the metal. Its action on wood is quite different from that of the mineral oils, for it closes up the pores and expands as it oxidizes. Linseed oil and elbow grease will maintain the perfect polish of the stock so that it even improves with years of use.

Sometimes external or internal rust occurs on a

gun that has been carelessly stored. If the damage is not serious it can be dealt with without a visit to the gunmaker. To remove rust, either wrap in bandages soaked with paraffin oil (Kerosene in American), or else use boiling water and scald well inside and out.

Either treatment kills the rust and makes it easily removable, but after using either paraffin or hot water the barrels must be most scrupulously dried off and oiled all over with good gun oil.

When guns are put away in their cases care should be taken that they are properly cleaned and vaselined first. Also it is important to make sure that the cases themselves are dry, and it is always as well to " air " them in hot sun or before a good fire.

When packing a gun in its case for travelling, care should be taken that everything fits perfectly and that nothing can move or rattle. The little oil bottle should be filled and secured, and a valuable field accessory is a simple pull-through brush on the end of a string. The weight on the string is simply dropped through the barrel from the breech end and the brush pulled straight through. This precaution at the end of a day's shooting takes no time and is of material value, for the cleaning of the guns is often left to the keeper and he may put it off to the next morning.

The cleaning of rifles is more difficult than that of shot-guns, for there is an added difficulty from the presence of metallic fouling or nickelling. Rifles should be cleaned with special anti-fouling liquids or cordite-cleansers. These contain elements that neutralize the acid residues of the powders and remove the nickelling. The old way of scouring out with boiling-hot water is, however, far the best and most reliable. Even when a rifle has been cleaned it should be re-cleaned just as thoroughly two days later, for the metal has a tendency to absorb the acids which later sweat up as a rust. As a corrosion preventive the excellent paste made by the B.S.A. can be used, for if the barrels are left coated with this no further corrosion can take place. This B.S.A. " Safety-Paste " is decidedly valuable and a blessing to the indolent man, and is equally useful on shot-guns as well as rifles.

The gun case itself should be worthy of the gun and should be a stout oak frame, leather-covered and brass-cornered. A further external cover of Willesden canvas is an additional precaution. The plain canvas gun covers or the light " leg-of-mutton cases " give little protection to a gun, though they are convenient for stowing in a car.

Ammunition should be kept in the special cartridge magazines made for the purpose. The size to carry 300 is ample for most purposes, and additional supplies can be taken direct in the wooden boxes in which they are supplied.

Although shooting clothes are not kept in the gun-room they are a subject often discussed there. For shooting, comfortable clothes and above all comfortable boots are all-essential. Boots for shooting should be old, supple, well-greased and well-nailed, and do up with eyelets in place of hooks. The laces should pass through a leather loop at the back to prevent them working up over the tops and the tongue should reach right to the top of the boot. A properly broken-in pair of army ammunition boots well greased and worn, with a good thick wool sock or stocking, makes as fine a shooting boot as any. Canvas anklets or spats should be worn to prevent heather or burs from working down inside the boot.

93

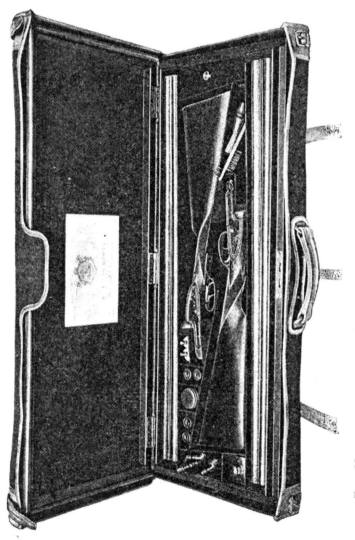

FIG. 25.—THE IDEAL EQUIPMENT. A PAIR OF CHURCHILL GUNS COMPLETE IN LEATHER CASE AND WITH TRAVELLING COVER AND ACCESSORIES

For the legs stockings are the usual wear, but many shooters prefer stout leather gaiters which are warmer in winter and also keep off a deal of cold water in high kale or roots. Knickerbockers should be loose and roomy at the knee instead of the tight riding breeches type, and of stout material. The design of shooting-coats is an art in itself, for it is all essential to have the coat light and free so that the arms can have full swing. To this end, then, the coat should not be tight across the chest or at the waist, but should be free to lift without the slightest pull when the arms are raised. The pockets should be placed conveniently for slipping the hand into for cartridges, but the large game pocket lined with blood-proof material that is favoured by keepers is unnecessary for the ordinary man, for it is not much use having a coat loose anywhere if you weight it down with 8 lb. or 9 lb. of game. If the pocket is deemed useful it should be at the back of the coat over the left buttock, for there the drag of the weight is taken on the left shoulder leaving the right comparatively free.

The English shooting season runs from August to February, and any temperature from sweltering heat to ice cold may happen in the season. To this end, then, one shooting suit is unlikely to be ideal for all conditions, and a light shower-proof coat is needed besides the heavier one. Some of Burberry's thin materials for semi-tropical use are excellent for this. For under-garments wool and flannel are the only safe wear, cotton is alluring in a hot September, but it undeniably means chills or rheumatism later.

For wet weather a light Burberry is the best shooting overall, and a silk handkerchief should be kept

95

permanently in its pocket for tucking in round one's neck in heavy rain.

The colour of shooting clothes is very important and difficult to decide as backgrounds vary so much in hue. The light greyish tweeds are good, particularly when interspersed with blues and greens. Dark suits even in mixed colours are very much more visible than light ones. For work in Scotland the Lovat mixtures or the dark heather-browns of the Western Isles are excellent, but all these tend to stand out very much more darkly when wet. It is a paradox that the cloth which seems too light at the tailors is usually too dark when viewed under field conditions.

The practice of camouflage in war teaches us that for objects moving with varying backgrounds patched effects, chocolate-brown where the strong lights fall, and cream-light where there are natural shadows, are the best. The mottling of animals and the fact that all their under parts, which are normally in shadow, are lighter than the salient parts, points to broken colour effects as being more suitable. As a camouflage suit would look more than a little extraordinary, a compromise can be made by wearing odd jacket, waistcoat, knee-breeches and stockings, thus trusting to the various shades to blend with surrounding natural lights and shadows so as to break up the general outline.

The other essentials for shooting are a stout pig-skin cartridge bag capable of holding 100 12-bore cases and a shooting stick with a seat handle. Of these the ordinary aluminium pattern is the best, and it can be provided with a light strap so that it can be conveniently slung over the shoulder out of one's way when walking up a field.

# GUNROOM, ACCESSORIES, AND DRESS

When waiting for driven birds, or outside the edge of a cover, a shooting seat is an absolute godsend, and the slight rests so obtained enable a much longer day to be gone through without fatigue.

Some shooters suffer from gun-headache and find no remedy in changes of powder. This troublesome ailment is due more to recoil than anything, and I am told that an excellent way of avoiding it is a simple rubber elastic band kept in the mouth and gripped between the teeth while shooting. Though I am not familiar with the device, it may prove worth knowing to those who seek alleviation from such a sport spoiling trouble.

Re-loading sporting cartridges is seldom practised in England except by keepers, all particulars with regard to powder loads and outfits can be found in the older sporting books, but so far as the ordinary man is concerned the economy is not worth the waste of time, and the results are inferior to ordinary professional work.

The keeping of game registers and full accounts of the shoot is an important gunroom function, and the records thus obtained over a series of years are extremely interesting. The volumes on " Shooting " of the Badminton Library will afford excellent examples of game records of their period, but, quite apart from the interest of estate records so kept, one's personal register of bags is even more absorbing. Such a record need not be merely a numerical register of the bag, but may well contain a note of the members of the party, and small details that will be of interest and serve to waken memories when read years hence. Indeed, it should be a diary of shooting days, and to a sportsman such is always pleasant reading.

# CHAPTER VIII

## SHOOTING

THE only way to learn shooting is by continual practice in the field from a comparatively early age. Good natural shots are born rather than made, but it is well within the compass of the average man to become a good average shot even if he has done little shot-gun work before. Nowadays the shooting school is resorted to not only by novices, but by many good shots who like to have a run through to put them into practice before the season starts.

Shooting schools are useful for instruction and for practice, but their limit of usefulness is soon reached because the " clay " pigeons used as targets behave quite differently from the normal birds, for " clays " start at high speed and then slow down. By increasing the power of the traps, and the height of the towers, very high speed can be attained by the clays, and good modern machines can be set to project the " birds " at almost any speed or angle.

Clay-bird shooting may admittedly be made as difficult as real shooting, but it cannot by any stretch of circumstances be held to compare with real shooting, for the conditions are entirely different.

At a shooting school a novice can be taught how to use and handle a gun, and how to hit simple moving objects. Above all he learns *how* his gun shoots. At the school he lays the foundation of all shooting skill— quick instinctive action of eye, brain, and hand. The modern shooting school has its ranges laid out to give a variety of effects. Traps in pits or trenches simulate

# SHOOTING

the conditions of walling-up game. Driven birds can be sent at a shooter over a wall or hedge, high birds are thrown from towers, and all forms of crossing and rising shot are reproduced.

Thus a novice who goes through a short course at a shooting school has everything to learn in the field, but can yet take his place at a small shoot without lack of self-confidence. Most gunmakers have private shooting grounds or schools within easy distance of London, and a morning spent at clays with a new gun or even as practice with an old friend before the season is not expensive, and well worth while the time and money expended.

It is quite impossible to explain in so many words how to shoot, and all that can be done is to give certain general rules, the exact application of which can only be learnt through practice.

The easiest shot of all is probably the slow pheasant walked up in cover, and going in an almost direct line away from the guns.

So far as can be judged from old sporting books and prints, shots of the early Victorian era were mostly of this nature, but this is possibly very largely an artist's convention. Sportsmen went out with their well-trained dogs and their muzzle-loaders, and the birds were routed up from the thick knee-high stubble that prevailed before modern methods of reaping were introduced.

To-day not only methods of shooting have changed, but the habits of game have changed owing to the old long stubbles having been done away with by the mechanical harvester, and to the fact that root crops, such as turnips, are nowadays sown in rows. A good forty years has failed to eradicate the superstition that walking up birds in cover is the most sportsmanlike method of shooting them, but when the facts are faced it must be at once admitted that driven birds are twice as hard to hit.

The best early training practice for a novice before he begins general shooting is to my mind shots at the

By the courtesy of Fig. 26 Messrs. Joseph Lang

AN OLD-FASHIONED SHOOTING GALLERY

humb'e rabbit *in cover*. In the open he is easy, but through bracken and bramble, where only a part of the target is visible for a fractional part of a second, the rabbit is not an easy shot. Gamekeepers and others attain an almost infallible accuracy at the rabbit, and fail at birds to the shooting of which they are not accustomed, but nevertheless, as practice, the rabbit is neither to be despised nor neglected.

Hares, on the other hand, are easy when they offer crossing shots, for swing the gun with its bead on the head of the hare and it is almost certain, but take them coming towards you or going away and it is remarkable how easy it is to miss. Long shots at hares should always be avoided, for it is better that the beast should get away than that it should be wounded and suffer. For the hare going away direct, or at an awkward angle, 30 yds. may be deemed the limit of range. Beyond this there is little chance of killing, and merciful self-restraint is the better practice. With hares coming close toward one a shot at the ground level, 6 in. in front of one, is likely to be the best.

Here it may be said that no one man's estimate of range or allowance coincides with another's. Personally I find it impossible to explain why I shoot straight at all, but all that I can say is that experience has taught me to give certain allowances for different shots. The apparent distances that I allow may not suit anyone else, for what I imagine to be a 6 in. allowance may be 24 in. for all I know. The sovereign rule is to centre upon one bird and one alone, concentrate all one's attention upon it and aim, or rather " mentally remember " that one's aim should be at *the beak*. *Nine-tenths of the game that is missed is missed because the shots go behind or under.*

The walked up birds going straight away are best for beginners, for there a straight foresight slap on the top of the rump always kills.

Sight of the foresight alone will not effect this if half the barrels are seen as well. For the normal English shot the cheek must touch the wood of the stock at the instant of firing, and then, if the gun fits, only the last inch of the barrels and the sight will be seen over the standing breech.

Some folk shoot with an erect neck—notably Americans, and for the straight-necked shooter a gun with a deeper bend and dropped comb is an essential. This is one of the reasons why your gunmaker should see you shoot as well as look you over, for the straight-necked shot will bend to aim when he remembers it, and a mere movement or two in a gunmaker's shop is not enough to show how one really shoots if one has an early habit such as erect or two-eyed shooting instinctively ingrained into one's nature.

Simple crossing and rising birds are the next step, and they need allowance high, and proportionate *swing* in front. This swing varies with the performer, but at ranges of 30 yds. odd a mental conception of shooting a few inches in front of the bird's beak is all that one needs with a swinging shot. Experience will teach just the right allowance, and once having found out what it is, do your level best to remember it as a standard, for once you have found it a very little mental concentration will make you allow for it in future without any coherent thought process and purely by instinctive or automatic co-operation of eye, hand, and muscular movement.

With driven birds a great deal more skill and quickness is necessary than with slow-rising walked up shots. The birds are upon and over you in a flash, and, in order to kill in front of you in a good workmanlike manner, you need to have a considerable degree of skill.

The thing to aim at is to realize or rather *to anticipate the moment at which the selected bird becomes most shootable.* With every bird there is one fractional moment when he is best situated with regard to your chance of a shot, and with driven birds nine-tenths of the art is the recognition or anticipation of the precise moment when the bird you select will be at your best point for shooting. The pressing of the trigger with no recognized aim at the bird, but with the anticipation of his arriving at the point where the shot go just at the right moment, should follow almost instinctively.

The preceding paragraph seems gloriously vague, but it is about all that one can say. Before writing it I wandered round to half a dozen decent game shots of my acquaintance and asked them the direct question : " How would you explain to a fellow how to shoot driven partridges ? " and they were all both incoherent and inarticulate. Two of them were writers of admitted merit, but even the habit of putting consecutive thought to paper could not help them. The fact is that all shooting is a knack learnt by experience, and communicable only through practice and a correct diagnosis of one's faults. Here the old hand can help you if you are in doubt, and Old Bill's immortal question : " Where did that one go ? " addressed to the keeper or loader behind you is more real help for correction than all the words set in type.

The high bird or the " rocketter," which is a high bird moving toward the shooter, is admittedly the most difficult shot. The proportion of misses is increased by the fact that most people start, or half start, a mental calculation about the beast, and if you try to calculate it is odds on that you will not hit.

The one thing to remember with the difficult shot is not the allowance, but to get well down to the gun, cheek on the stalk and foresight bead central along the rib. According to theory 1 ft. allowance for every 5 yds. of range is the true allowance, but in practice the shot swing or lateral movement one gives to the gun compensates for much of this, and one learns to allow so many bird-lengths for the apparent size of the bird at distances. Thus, at an apparently long bird five " bird-lengths " may be no unnecessary allowance. High birds appear much more distant than they really are, particularly when topping trees. Birds over the tops of trees are seldom more than 30 yds. high, and even in those difficult shoots where birds rising in the sharp sides of a hill cover or stream-cut valley rise 20 ft. from the shooter's level toward the tree tops, they usually come down in their flight toward the opposite side, and the bird of 35 to 40 yds. high is seldom met with.

The fixed dimension that the normal shot sees is the width of both barrels at their tip with the central foresight giving a median point. Whatever the range of the bird this dimension does not vary, and the probable mental calculation which is instinctive and therefore unfollowable is so many " barrel widths " allowance for high and crossing birds at different ranges. Now the space covered by a barrel width at 15 yds. is much less than the space covered at 30, but somehow or other the brain learns to adjust these distances or visual angles without conscious thought, and takes into consideration the fact that the further a bird is away the longer time one has to shoot in.

The whole essence of " style " in shooting birds, is a correct estimation of time as well as allowance. With every bird there is a best moment, and, where in walking up one shoots slowly, with driven birds early shots are better.

With practice one becomes able to anticipate the right moment, and a clean neat kill results.

Above all, in shooting try to kill clean. A man who kills his bird is worth twice the man who brings down more, but many of them " runners." Wounded birds not only are a cause of regret to the sportsman, but delay the whole shoot until they are run down by the dogs. Sometimes they are unavoidable, but on the whole it is always worth sacrificing doubtful shots in order to avoid them.

The literature on shooting topics is both discursive and voluminous, and the older books are so good that with the exception of their sections upon the " modern " weapons of their day they leave little to be brought up to date. To the shooting man books on shooting will always possess a definite appeal and charm that other and better written works fail to yield. The value of them, so far as the modern shot is concerned, varies with the interpretative skill of the reader, but Chaucer was not wrong when he held that—

> "—Out of old bookes in good faith
> Cometh all this new science that men lere."

The two volumes of the Badminton Library on shooting : (1) *Field and Covert*, (2) *Moor and Marsh*, are still standards. *The Gun and Its Development*, by W. W. Greener, is the standard work on arms and cannot be surpassed. *Deer Stalking*, by Augustus Grimble, is probably the best work of its kind, and Colonel Hawker's *Instructions to Young Shooters* is still the wild-fowler's companion.

All of these are old books—and good books, while *A Shooting Catechism*, by Colonel R. F. Meysey Thompson, is more recent but earnestly to be recommended. The *Notes on Shooting*, issued by Nobels Explosives, Ltd., is not a text-book but just notes that no shooter would willingly be without, for it gives all that is latest in simple technics, and a good deal of excellent general information readable from cover to cover. Charles Lancaster's illustrated treatise

105

on the *Art of Shooting* is a great help to the young shot, and for the companion weapon to the gun and rifle— the pistol—I shamelessly recommend my own book *The Book of the Pistol.* For periodicals, *Country Life* and the *Field* are stand-bys. The American journals are interesting, and *Outdoor Life,* a monthly magazine from Denver, Colorado, is by far the best of them.

This book is meant for a short popular handbook rather than an encyclopaedia, and it is meant for the average shooter rather than for experts. There are sins of omission as well as sins of commission. I may have sacrificed explicitness to clarity, and I have laid down as dogma many contentious things, but the limits of length laid down by the publishers, and my general idea of providing a modern up-to-date booklet on sporting arms, forbade a greater consumption of space and a more latitudinarian attitude toward vexed and delightful problems.

I tender due acknowledgment and thanks to all previous writers on sporting shooting, and to the several gunsmiths who have answered my many questions and helped me in many ways.

Material important to the shooter, but not in keeping with the run of the text, I have incorporated in the various Appendices ; fuller information may be sought in the works mentioned in this chapter, or on matters of guns or ammunition by direct application to the firms concerned.

No one of them is mentioned for advertising reasons, and I have no interest in any of them.

# APPENDIX

## SHOT-GUN DATA AND TABLES

*[Reprinted from "The Shooter's Year Book" by permission of Nobel Industries Ltd.]*

### BORES OF GUNS

| Description. | Diameter of Card Wadding. | Usual Case Lengths. | Gun Weight. |
|---|---|---|---|
| | in. | in. | lbs. |
| 4 bore . . . | ·948 | 4 | 14–18 |
| 8 ,, . . . | ·845 | $3\frac{1}{4}$–$4\frac{1}{4}$ | 10–13 |
| 10 ,, . . . | ·784 | $2\frac{5}{8}$–$2\frac{7}{8}$ | 8–9 |
| 12 ,, . . . | ·738 | $2\frac{1}{2}$–3 | 6–8 |
| 14 ,, . . . | ·702 | $2\frac{1}{2}$ | $6\frac{1}{4}$ |
| 16 ,, . . . | ·671 | $2\frac{1}{2}$–$2\frac{3}{4}$ | 6–$6\frac{1}{2}$ |
| 20 ,, . . . | ·623 | $2\frac{1}{2}$–$2\frac{3}{4}$ | $5\frac{1}{2}$–6 |
| 24 ,, . . . | ·587 | $2\frac{1}{2}$ | 5 |
| 28 ,, . . . | ·557 | $2\frac{1}{2}$ | $4\frac{3}{4}$ |
| 32 ,, . . . | ·509 | $2\frac{1}{2}$ | 4 |
| ·410 ,, . . . | ·415 | 2–$2\frac{1}{2}$ | $3\frac{3}{4}$ |
| ·360 ,, . . . | ·363 | $1\frac{3}{4}$ | — |
| No. 3 L.S. . . . | ·305 | 1–$1\frac{3}{4}$ | — |

*Note.*—The $2\frac{1}{2}$ inch case is actually $2\frac{9}{17}$ in. long in 12, 16, and 20-bore sizes. In other calibres the nominal length is also the real.

## DETAILS OF SHOT SIZES

| Designation. | Pellets per oz. | Weight per Pellet. | Diameter. | Value of " C." |
|---|---|---|---|---|
|  |  | grains. | inch. |  |
| LG | Approx. 6 | 70·0 | ·360 | ·690 |
| MG | 7 | 62·5 | ·347 | ·0663 |
| SG | 8 | 54·7 | ·332 | ·0634 |
| Special SG | 11 | 39·8 | ·298 | ·0572 |
| SSG | 15 | 29·17 | ·269 | ·0514 |
| SSSG | 20 | 21·89 | ·245 | ·0464 |
| SSSSG | 25 | 17·50 | ·227 | ·0433 |
| SSSSSG | 30 | 14·58 | ·214 | ·0407 |
| AAA | 35 | 12·50 | ·203 | ·0387 |
| AA | 40 | 10·94 | ·194 | ·0370 |
| A | 50 | 8·75 | ·180 | ·0344 |
| BBB | 60 | 7·29 | ·170 | ·0321 |
| BB | 70 | 6·25 | ·161 | ·0307 |
| B | 80 | 5·47 | ·154 | ·0297 |
| 1 | 100 | 4·38 | ·143 | ·0273 |
| 2 | 120 | 3·65 | ·135 | ·0255 |
| 3 | 140 | 3·12 | ·128 | ·0243 |
| 4 | 170 | 2·57 | ·120 | ·0228 |
| 4½ | 200 | 2·19 | ·113 | ·0218 |
| 5 | 220 | 1·99 | ·110 | ·0210 |
| 5½ | 240 | 1·82 | ·107 | ·0203 |
| 6 | 272 | 1·61 | ·102 | ·0197 |
| 6½ | 300 | 1·46 | ·099 | ·0190 |
| 7 | 340 | 1·29 | ·095 | ·0182 |
| 8 | 450 | ·97 | ·087 | ·0163 |
| 9 | 580 | ·75 | ·080 | ·0149 |
| 10 | 850 | ·51 | ·070 | ·0133 |

# PELLETS IN GAME CHARGES

| Oz. of Shot. | Size of Shot. | | | | | | |
|---|---|---|---|---|---|---|---|
| | 4 | 4½ | 5 | 5½ | 6 | 6½ | 7 |
| 1½ | 255 | 300 | 330 | 360 | 408 | 450 | 510 |
| 1 7/16 | 244 | 288 | 316 | 345 | 391 | 431 | 489 |
| 1 3/8 | 234 | 275 | 303 | 330 | 374 | 413 | 468 |
| 1 5/16 | 223 | 263 | 289 | 315 | 357 | 394 | 446 |
| 1 ¼ | 213 | 250 | 275 | 300 | 340 | 375 | 425 |
| 1 3/16 | 202 | 238 | 261 | 285 | 323 | 356 | 404 |
| 1 ⅛ | 191 | 225 | 248 | 270 | 306 | 338 | 383 |
| 1 1/16 | 181 | 213 | 234 | 255 | 289 | 319 | 361 |
| One | 170 | 200 | 220 | 240 | 272 | 300 | 340 |
| 15/16 | 159 | 188 | 206 | 225 | 255 | 281 | 319 |
| ⅞ | 149 | 175 | 193 | 210 | 238 | 263 | 298 |
| 13/16 | 138 | 163 | 179 | 195 | 221 | 244 | 276 |
| ¾ | 128 | 150 | 165 | 180 | 204 | 225 | 255 |
| 11/16 | 117 | 138 | 151 | 165 | 187 | 206 | 234 |
| ⅝ | 106 | 125 | 138 | 150 | 170 | 187 | 212 |
| 9/16 | 96 | 113 | 124 | 135 | 153 | 169 | 191 |
| ½ | 85 | 100 | 110 | 120 | 136 | 150 | 170 |

PELLETS IN 30 in. CIRCLE STANDARD LOADS
(1⅛ oz. SHOT)

| Conditions. | Range in Yards. | | | | | | |
|---|---|---|---|---|---|---|---|
| | **30** | **35** | **40** | **45** | **50** | **55** | **60** |
| **No. 4 Shot (181 pellets) :** | | | | | | | |
| True Cylinder . . | 108 | 89 | 72 | 59 | 47 | 38 | 30 |
| Improved Cylinder . | 129 | 110 | 91 | 75 | 60 | 48 | 39 |
| Half Choke . . . | 151 | 129 | 109 | 91 | 73 | 59 | 48 |
| Full Choke . . . | 172 | 148 | 127 | 108 | 86 | 70 | 57 |
| **No. 5 Shot (234 pellets) :** | | | | | | | |
| True Cylinder . . | 140 | 115 | 94 | 77 | 61 | 49 | 39 |
| Improved Cylinder . | 167 | 142 | 117 | 97 | 77 | 62 | 50 |
| Half Choke . . . | 195 | 167 | 140 | 118 | 94 | 76 | 62 |
| Full Choke . . . | 223 | 192 | 163 | 139 | 111 | 90 | 74 |
| **No. 6 Shot (289 pellets) :** | | | | | | | |
| True Cylinder . . | 173 | 142 | 114 | 95 | 75 | 60 | 49 |
| Improved Cylinder . | 208 | 175 | 145 | 120 | 95 | 77 | 62 |
| Half Choke . . . | 241 | 206 | 176 | 146 | 116 | 94 | 76 |
| Full Choke . . . | 275 | 237 | 202 | 172 | 138 | 111 | 91 |
| **No. 7 Shot (361 pellets) :** | | | | | | | |
| True Cylinder . . | 215 | 177 | 144 | 118 | 94 | 75 | 61 |
| Improved Cylinder . | 258 | 218 | 181 | 150 | 119 | 96 | 78 |
| Half Choke . . . | 301 | 258 | 217 | 182 | 145 | 117 | 95 |
| Full Choke . . . | 344 | 296 | 253 | 215 | 172 | 139 | 114 |

## DIAMETER OF SPREAD

Being the diameter in inches covered by the whole charge of a gun at various Ranges for all calibres.

| Boring of Gun. | Range in Yards. | | | | | | |
|---|---|---|---|---|---|---|---|
| | 10 | 15 | 20 | 25 | 30 | 35 | 40 |
| True Cylinder . . . | 19 | 26 | 32 | 38 | 44 | 51 | 57 |
| Improved Cylinder . | 15 | 20 | 26 | 32 | 38 | 44 | 51 |
| Half Choke . . . | 12 | 16 | 20 | 26 | 32 | 38 | 46 |
| Full Choke . . . | 9 | 12 | 16 | 21 | 26 | 32 | 40 |

## TESTING PATTERN AT DIFFERENT RANGES

The pellets in a 30-in. circle will strike in the following size circles at less distances.

| Boring of Gun. | Range in Yards. | | | | | | |
|---|---|---|---|---|---|---|---|
| | 10 | 15 | 20 | 25 | 30 | 35 | 40 |
| Improved Cylinder . | 7·0 | 10·0 | 13·2 | 16·7 | 20·6 | 25·0 | 30 |
| Half Choke . . . | 6·3 | 9·0 | 12·1 | 15·7 | 19·8 | 24·5 | 30 |
| Full Choke . . . | 5·5 | 8·0 | 11·0 | 14·6 | 18·9 | 24·0 | 30 |

## TABLE OF ALLOWANCES

For aiming in front of Birds crossing at 40 miles per hour, using Standard Game Cartridges.

| Size of Shot. | Range in Yards. | | | | | | | | | |
|---|---|---|---|---|---|---|---|---|---|---|
| | 20 | | 25 | | 30 | | 35 | | 40 | |
| | ft. | in. | ft. | in. | ft. | in. | ft. | in. | ft. | in. |
| 3 | 3 | 8·0 | 4 | 7·4 | 5 | 9·6 | 6 | 11·7 | 8 | 2·6 |
| 4 | 3 | 8·0 | 4 | 8·6 | 5 | 10·2 | 7 | 0·7 | 8 | 4·1 |
| 5 | 3 | 8·0 | 4 | 8·7 | 5 | 10·5 | 7 | 1·2 | 8 | 4·9 |
| 5½ | 3 | 8·0 | 4 | 8·8 | 5 | 10·7 | 7 | 1·6 | 8 | 5·6 |
| 6 | 3 | 8·0 | 4 | 8·9 | 5 | 10·9 | 7 | 2·0 | 8 | 6·1 |
| 6½ | 3 | 8·0 | 4 | 9·0 | 5 | 11·1 | 7 | 2·4 | 8 | 6·7 |
| 7 | 3 | 8·0 | 4 | 9·1 | 5 | 11·4 | 7 | 2·8 | 8 | 7·3 |

## APPROXIMATE ALLOWANCES

| All Sizes | 4 ft. | 5 ft. | 6 ft. | 7 ft. | 8–9 ft. |
|---|---|---|---|---|---|

# COMPARISON OF STANDARD BRITISH GAME CARTRIDGES GIVING DIFFERENT GRADES OF VELOCITY

## 1. VERY HIGH VELOCITY (1150 f.s.)

| | Range in Yards. | | | | | | |
| | 10 | 20 | 30 | 35 | 40 | 50 | 60 |
|---|---|---|---|---|---|---|---|
| Striking Velocity f.s. | 1120 | 903 | 759 | 701 | 649 | 562 | 489 |
| Pellet Energy in ft.-lbs. | 4·47 | 2·91 | 2·06 | 1·75 | 1·50 | 1·13 | ·85 |
| Forward Allowance in feet | 1·3 | 3·1 | 5·3 | 6·6 | 7·9 | 10·9 | 14·3 |

## 2. STANDARD VELOCITY (1050 f.s.)

| | Range in Yards. | | | | | | |
| | 10 | 20 | 30 | 35 | 40 | 50 | 60 |
|---|---|---|---|---|---|---|---|
| Striking Velocity f.s. | 1026 | 845 | 716 | 662 | 615 | 534 | 466 |
| Pellet Energy in ft.-lbs. | 3·86 | 2·55 | 1·83 | 1·56 | 1·35 | 1·02 | ·77 |
| Forward Allowance in feet | 1·5 | 3·4 | 5·7 | 7·1 | 8·5 | 11·6 | 15·2 |

## 3. LOW VELOCITY (950 f.s.)

| | Range in Yards. | | | | | | |
| | 10 | 20 | 30 | 35 | 40 | 50 | 60 |
|---|---|---|---|---|---|---|---|
| Striking Velocity f.s. | 932 | 780 | 665 | 617 | 575 | 500 | 437 |
| Pellet Energy in ft.-lbs. | 3·10 | 2·1 | 1·58 | 1·36 | 1·18 | ·89 | ·68 |
| Forward Allowance in feet | 1·7 | 3·8 | 6·3 | 7·7 | 9·2 | 12·6 | 16·4 |

## TRUE CYLINDER ( = 40%) PATTERNS

| Oz. of Shot. | Pellets in 30 in. circle at 40 YARDS for different SIZES of Shot. | | | | | | |
|---|---|---|---|---|---|---|---|
| | 4 | 4½ | 5 | 5½ | 6 | 6½ | 7 |
| 1½ | 102 | 120 | 132 | 144 | 163 | 180 | 204 |
| 1 7/16 | 97 | 115 | 126 | 138 | 156 | 172 | 196 |
| 1 3/8 | 94 | 110 | 121 | 132 | 150 | 165 | 187 |
| 1 5/16 | 89 | 105 | 116 | 126 | 143 | 158 | 178 |
| 1 ¼ | 85 | 100 | 110 | 120 | 136 | 150 | 170 |
| 1 3/16 | 81 | 95 | 104 | 114 | 129 | 142 | 162 |
| 1 ⅛ | 76 | 90 | 99 | 108 | 122 | 135 | 153 |
| 1 1/16 | 72 | 85 | 94 | 102 | 116 | 128 | 144 |
| One | 68 | 80 | 88 | 96 | 109 | 120 | 136 |
| 15/16 | 64 | 75 | 82 | 90 | 102 | 112 | 128 |
| ⅞ | 60 | 70 | 77 | 84 | 95 | 105 | 119 |
| 13/16 | 55 | 65 | 72 | 78 | 88 | 98 | 110 |
| ¾ | 51 | 60 | 66 | 72 | 82 | 90 | 102 |
| 11/16 | 47 | 55 | 60 | 66 | 75 | 82 | 94 |
| ⅝ | 42 | 50 | 55 | 60 | 68 | 75 | 85 |
| 9/16 | 38 | 45 | 50 | 54 | 61 | 68 | 76 |
| ½ | 34 | 40 | 44 | 48 | 54 | 60 | 69 |

# IMPROVED CYLINDER ( = 50%) PATTERNS

| Oz. of Shot. | Pellets in 30 in. circle at 40 YARDS for different SIZES of Shot. | | | | | | |
|---|---|---|---|---|---|---|---|
| | 4 | 4½ | 5 | 5½ | 6 | 6½ | 7 |
| 1½ | 128 | 150 | 165 | 180 | 204 | 225 | 255 |
| 1 7⁄16 | 212 | 144 | 158 | 173 | 196 | 216 | 245 |
| 1⅜ | 117 | 138 | 152 | 165 | 187 | 207 | 234 |
| 1 5⁄16 | 111 | 132 | 145 | 158 | 179 | 197 | 223 |
| 1¼ | 107 | 125 | 138 | 150 | 170 | 188 | 213 |
| 1 3⁄16 | 101 | 119 | 131 | 143 | 162 | 178 | 202 |
| 1⅛ | 96 | 113 | 124 | 135 | 153 | 169 | 192 |
| 1 1⁄16 | 91 | 107 | 117 | 128 | 145 | 160 | 181 |
| One | 85 | 100 | 110 | 120 | 136 | 150 | 170 |
| 15⁄16 | 80 | 94 | 103 | 113 | 128 | 141 | 160 |
| ⅞ | 75 | 88 | 97 | 105 | 119 | 132 | 149 |
| 13⁄16 | 69 | 82 | 90 | 98 | 111 | 122 | 138 |
| ¾ | 64 | 75 | 83 | 90 | 102 | 113 | 128 |
| 11⁄16 | 59 | 69 | 76 | 83 | 94 | 103 | 117 |
| ⅝ | 53 | 63 | 69 | 75 | 85 | 94 | 106 |
| 9⁄16 | 48 | 57 | 62 | 68 | 77 | 85 | 96 |
| ½ | 43 | 50 | 55 | 60 | 68 | 75 | 85 |

## HALF CHOKE ( = 60%) PATTERNS

| Oz. of Shot. | Pellets in 30 in. circle at 40 YARDS for different SIZES of Shot. | | | | | | |
|---|---|---|---|---|---|---|---|
| | 4 | 4½ | 5 | 5½ | 6 | 6½ | 7 |
| $1\frac{1}{2}$ | 153 | 180 | 198 | 216 | 244 | 270 | 306 |
| $1\frac{7}{16}$ | 146 | 173 | 189 | 207 | 235 | 259 | 294 |
| $1\frac{3}{8}$ | 140 | 165 | 182 | 198 | 224 | 248 | 280 |
| $1\frac{5}{16}$ | 134 | 158 | 174 | 189 | 214 | 236 | 267 |
| $1\frac{1}{4}$ | 128 | 150 | 165 | 180 | 204 | 225 | 255 |
| $1\frac{3}{16}$ | 121 | 142 | 157 | 171 | 194 | 214 | 242 |
| $1\frac{1}{8}$ | 115 | 135 | 148 | 162 | 184 | 203 | 230 |
| $1\frac{1}{16}$ | 109 | 128 | 140 | 153 | 173 | 191 | 217 |
| One | 102 | 120 | 132 | 144 | 163 | 180 | 204 |
| $\frac{15}{16}$ | 95 | 112 | 124 | 135 | 153 | 169 | 191 |
| $\frac{7}{8}$ | 89 | 105 | 115 | 126 | 143 | 158 | 179 |
| $\frac{13}{16}$ | 83 | 98 | 108 | 117 | 133 | 146 | 166 |
| $\frac{3}{4}$ | 77 | 90 | 99 | 108 | 122 | 135 | 153 |
| $\frac{11}{16}$ | 70 | 82 | 91 | 99 | 112 | 124 | 140 |
| $\frac{5}{8}$ | 64 | 75 | 82 | 90 | 102 | 112 | 127 |
| $\frac{9}{16}$ | 58 | 68 | 74 | 81 | 92 | 102 | 115 |
| $\frac{1}{2}$ | 51 | 60 | 66 | 72 | 81 | 90 | 102 |

## FULL CHOKE ( = 70%) PATTERNS

| Oz. of Shot. | Pellets in 30 in. circle at 40 YARDS for different SIZES of Shot. | | | | | | |
|---|---|---|---|---|---|---|---|
| | 4 | 4½ | 5 | 5½ | 6 | 6½ | 7 |
| 1 ½ | 178 | 210 | 231 | 252 | 286 | 315 | 357 |
| 1 7/16 | 170 | 202 | 221 | 241 | 274 | 302 | 342 |
| 1 3/8 | 163 | 192 | 212 | 231 | 261 | 289 | 328 |
| 1 5/16 | 156 | 184 | 202 | 220 | 249 | 275 | 312 |
| 1 ¼ | 149 | 175 | 192 | 210 | 238 | 263 | 298 |
| 1 3/16 | 142 | 167 | 183 | 200 | 226 | 249 | 283 |
| 1 ⅛ | 134 | 157 | 174 | 189 | 214 | 236 | 268 |
| 1 1/16 | 127 | 149 | 163 | 179 | 202 | 223 | 253 |
| One | 119 | 140 | 154 | 168 | 190 | 210 | 238 |
| 15/16 | 112 | 132 | 144 | 158 | 179 | 197 | 223 |
| ⅞ | 105 | 122 | 135 | 147 | 167 | 184 | 209 |
| 13/16 | 97 | 114 | 125 | 137 | 155 | 171 | 194 |
| ¾ | 90 | 105 | 115 | 126 | 143 | 158 | 179 |
| 11/16 | 81 | 97 | 106 | 115 | 130 | 144 | 163 |
| ⅝ | 75 | 87 | 97 | 105 | 119 | 130 | 148 |
| 9/16 | 67 | 79 | 86 | 94 | 107 | 118 | 134 |
| ½ | 59 | 70 | 77 | 86 | 95 | 105 | 119 |

# CHURCHILL

Guns are built to order. We also keep a stock of guns finished with the exception of shaping the stock, therefore normal requirements may be supplied within a few days.

## FOUR MODELS

AT

## £100, £80, £60 & £45

*Specialities recommended :*

1. The " XXV " (25″ barrels) maximum strength and shooting qualities combined with extra light weight and improved balance. An inestimable aid to good shooting.

2. The improved type of " Over and Under " action, which is the neatest and strongest yet introduced.

Catalogues and lists, including Second-hand Guns and Rifles, Shooting Grounds, Guncases, Cartridges, and all requisites for Game or Trap Shooting, free on request.

E. J. CHURCHILL (Gun Makers) Ltd.,
8 AGAR STREET, STRAND, LONDON, W.C.2

*Telephones :* Gerrard 2046, 2047 & 2586.     *Telegrams :* "*Shawfowls-London*"

# SECOND HAND GUNS

## "EQUAL TO NEW"

## A STATEMENT.

WE affirm without hesitation and without fear of contradiction that we hold the largest, best selected, and most comprehensive stock of Second-hand Guns in the world. Our tradition is that success is bound up in the satisfaction of Customers; our slogan is "equal to new"; and our ambition is to be of service to all good sportsmen.

# C·B·VAUGHAN

## 39, STRAND, LONDON, W.C.2.

A STOCK OF OVER
**500 GUNS**
TO SELECT FROM
—
**EVERY WEAPON
GUARANTEED**

CATALOGUE "S"
POST FREE

# INDEX

# INDEX

PRINTED IN GREAT BRITAIN AT THE PITMAN PRESS, BATH
(Y—2196)

*By Appointment*

# CHARLES LANCASTER
## *&* Co., Ltd.

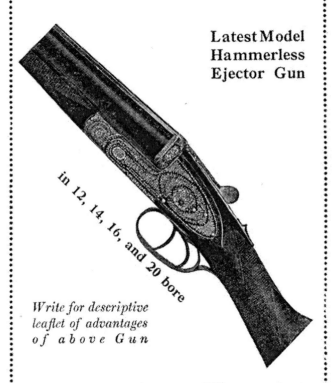

Latest Model
Hammerless
Ejector Gun

*in 12, 14, 16, and 20 bore*

*Write for descriptive
leaflet of advantages
of above Gun*

## 11 Panton Street, Haymarket
## London, S.W.1

TELEPHONE: GERRARD 3691

# AUTOMATIC
# =PISTOLS=

## By MAJOR HUGH B. C. POLLARD

*Author of "The Shot Gun," "The Book of the Pistol and Revolver," etc.*

## *In demy 8vo, cloth gilt. 6/-net*

A very complete history of the development of the Automatic Pistol, and a detailed description of all the principal models. Full directions for the use of automatics for self-defence and target work are included.

---

### SOME PRESS OPINIONS

THE FIELD : "We heartily endorse Major Pollard's remarks on shooting, and agree with him when he says that he believes that his views in the main are shared by all expert shots and shooting men. . . . The technical explanations of mechanism are on the whole able and sound. . . . The tables showing the comparative ballistics of the different makes are most interesting."

ARMS AND EXPLOSIVES : "The book as a whole we regard as perfect, and certainly well worth careful perusal by the many students of this fascinating branch of arms science. Whether or not it is read right away it should be on the library shelf."

HORSE AND HOUND : "Both expert and amateur are catered for in the book, which goes into the various phases of the subject pretty fully, and is undoubtedly an authoritative work."

SHOOTING GOODS REVIEW : "Major Pollard passes them all (the various makes of pistols) in review, explaining the main points of the different mechanisms, and expressing shrewd opinions from the personal standpoint of a critic who condemns what does not satisfy after trial, and praises what he finds to be good."

---

LONDON : SIR ISAAC PITMAN & SONS, LTD.

Printed in the United Kingdom
by Lightning Source UK Ltd.
135717UK00001B/84/A